CURSE OF THAT
LOTTERY TICKET

By

Zdenko Ornig

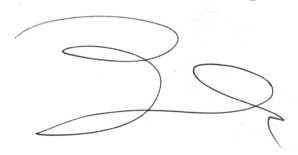

Foreword

This book is themed by the proverb of a cat
supposedly having nine lives.

As the reader, you may think that the series of events
occurring in this book border on the fantastical; sadly all the
unfolding chapters are in fact true.

Nothing written in this book has happened due to
deliberate misadventure, only the driving force of self-survival
which has occasionally led me into deadly situations.
More often than not, it was a case of wrong time, wrong place.

My thanks go to the following people for all their support:
my friend Joyce for her encouraging words; to Carl; to
Dr Sawyer for his endless understanding and Drs Friedman,
Irwine and Singh at St. Albans City Hospital; to Gabbi Draper
and Catherine Rose for their assistance in producing this
book; and of course, to Chris at Mansons Printers. Lastly, my
gratitude goes to the management of Betty Entwistle House
for their assistance and kindness.

Zdenko

Town: Maribor

Date of Birth: 1948

Year: 1962

9

That Lottery Ticket

A terribly loud noise woke me. It came from the first floor window of my room. There were at least ten of my forty racing pigeons, flapping and fighting on the ledge. Amongst them was a white one which was the first I had bought a year earlier with my pocket money. When he saw me, he flew away to a branch on the huge cherry tree that stood next to our house and then he returned. I sensed that he was trying to tell me something. Although his mate was beside him, he seemed bothered.

As he flew off again, I heard my father shouting in the next room: "Where is Olga?" Olga was my younger sister by two years.
I had never heard my father shout before. My mother replied loudly saying: "You just try! You just try!" I didn't have a clue what this was all about.

Then I heard the familiar sound of an automatic pistol being cocked. My mother screamed and shouted to me and my older brother Thomas, telling us to get out of the house as my father was going to kill us all.

I listened in total shock. All sorts of things were racing through my mind. Kill us all?
Why? For what reason? I knew that, as an officer in the Territorial Army, my father kept his armoury at home and always had his pistol at the ready. A year earlier Thomas had told me that he had found the pistol in my father's suitcase in my parents' room, and that he had fired it in the woods nearby with his friends. Thomas, two years my senior and in charge, forbade me to play with it on my own. Of course, I did not listen to him and on a few

occasions I did. The familiar sound of the click in the next room told me everything.

My pet pigeon, whom I had named Bixie, *had* been trying to tell me something. Within seconds of this realisation, I jumped onto the window ledge and from there onto the branch of the cherry tree where Bixie was perching. Although I was about twenty-five feet up, it took seconds to climb down to the ground. My mother was rearing chickens at the time, so I ran through their shed and climbed over the neighbour's fence to get as far away from home as possible.

By then, all the neighbours whose gardens bordered ours were looking out of their windows to see what was going on. The neighbour whose garden I found myself in was very insistent about calling the police which I did not want. All I was concerned about was my mother, Thomas and Olga's safety. I ran about half a mile to my aunty Hanika, who, when she saw me, crossed herself and thanked God for saving me. As she took me into her arms she said: "I knew something was going to happen".

My aunty had wanted to adopt me for years but my mother had said that because I was the most intelligent of her children, in no way would she let me go and live there, although she agreed that I could visit my aunty as much as possible. Aunty Hanika wasn't able to conceive due to diabetes and other ailments. She was well spoken and well read, and she never talked badly of my mother but she was concerned that my father trying to shoot us would have a psychological effect on me. Which it did.

After that shocking day, I did stay with my aunty and I did not go to school for two weeks. Mother kept coming to my aunt's house crying and begging for me to come home. After two days, she turned up with a package under her arm. All she said was that I must throw this heavily wrapped parcel in the river which was a few hundred yards away.

I took the package and headed for the river. I was certain that my mother had taken the pistol and wanted to get rid of it. Making sure I was not seen, I tied a few stones to the parcel so that it would sink to the lowest point of the deep and fast flowing river.

After half an hour I returned to my aunt's house. My mother was still there. Crying, I asked what had led to this near tragedy. Slowly and emotionally, she explained.

Apparently, three months previously, my father had gone to a show. There was a lottery at the end of the event. My father had taken chemicals used in his hobby as a photographer in order to change his raffle number to the winning one. The first prize was a motorcycle and just as the allotted ten minutes to present the ticket were up, and before the organisers could pick a replacement, my father stepped forward with his doctored one.

However, as he was about to wheel his prize away, the holder of the genuine ticket turned up, and to make matters worse, he was a policeman. It all went to court and my father was facing two years imprisonment. Because he was facing a custodial sentence and the loss of a key position in the textile industry where everybody knew him, he had seemingly 'lost the plot'.

The craziest thing about it was that he did not need to steal the motorcycle as with his wages he could afford to buy a new car every two years.

Within days of this event, my mother was called in to my school by the head to discuss my future education regarding my erratic attendance. I sat with my mother and we were informed of my only option. To my surprise and my mother's pride, it appeared I was going to be promoted instead of punished by being offered a tutorial position to my fellow pupils. This meant I would not have to face my father too often, and that I could compress two hourly lessons into one, bunk off to town and lose myself in the crowds in order to stay away from home. My plans were made.

I was given three classmates who were doing badly in four subjects: German, English, Mathematics and Physics. The classmate most urgently in need of improving his maths was a very quiet, tall, strong young man of my age by the name of Tony. He and his whole family had been forcibly resettled from another part of Slovenia, still a part of former Yugoslavia.

Under Tito's communist regime, in order to prevent any uprising amongst the population and due to extreme political and economic conditions immediately after the Second World War, many farm owners who had had strong connections with the Germans during the war or had very close German ancestry were automatically resettled and in many cases had their farms nationalised. Almost all of the farmers who had collaborated with the German army during the occupation were simply shot along with their families.

Tony was moved from the Adriatic part of Slovenia to our northern region. His family was given a farm with a lot of land and livestock. In return for this quota, seventy percent of their complete produce such as wheat, pork, beef, milk, corn, etc. was collected by the state, the tax being paid separately.

When I was introduced to Tony's father by the school head, it was apparent his parents were not happy with his extra lessons. They were actually very sad that their son was simply not coping with his studies. Financially, they had become far better off than most of the people around the village. I was to start my task the very next day.

When I came to their door, Tony's mother called me into a separate room and asked me how bad his marks were. I could not tell her since the results were kept locked in the head master's office. I gave her an indication that he was about to be dropped into a lower class, meaning he would have to repeat the class and be a whole year behind.

By coincidence, she had also met my mother and father and knew that I spent a lot of time at my aunt's house. I assumed that in a very small community people talk to each other. At the end of our conversation she stated that she felt sorry for me. Like most other people, she did not know the reason for my circumstances.

As we went into the dining room, Tony already had his books and writing pad in front of him which were spread over the big dining table. His mum asked me if she could sit with us for a while, although she didn't understand most of the material.

I began to ask Tony a few questions about certain points in the study books and realised we would have to start at the beginning. After about an hour, his mother looked at me with despair in her eyes. On that first day, we spent about three hours analysing where his problems were.

When his mother saw me out she gave me a carrier bag and whispered: "Because you look cold and hungry". I didn't know what to say. Here was a woman I had never met before giving me a woollen jumper (the thickest I had ever worn), a lump of cheese wrapped in Christmas paper, along with a big chunk of ham. She said: "Thank you, Zdenko, I know that Tony will make it with your help". She begged me not to abandon him as they had great admiration for my knowledge.

And so I went to Tony's farm twice a week in the afternoon. He did everything that I asked him to do. I also had two more pupils who needed a lot of patience. Back at school, I had regained my confidence, and the teachers were thrilled with the progress of my three pupils. I regained the respect and friendliness of everybody.

I had some bright moments at this young age as well. My father bought an accordion for my brother whom he doted on although he couldn't play and had no musical ear whatsoever. My mother insisted that I should be allowed to learn as well. I progressed very quickly and learned a lot of music. My father was disappointed that my brother only looked and listened at me playing that huge accordion. I couldn't even see the keyboard properly but I became better and better.

Over the long weekends, my mother always took me to our

granny's about ten miles away. My mother came from a big family. She had eleven siblings in total and they would all come together at my granny's so, to my mother's delight, I would entertain them with my musical talent. (Musical talent can't be taught or learned: it is something we are born with so no bragging here.)

Being from a Christian family, the custom was that a male guest should visit other's homes and wish them a Happy New Year. In a parallel class at my school were two older boys who invited me to join their duo. One played the trumpet and the other was a guitarist. They normally played on people's doorsteps in the early hours of New Year's Day. I was told that we would earn quite good money.

We got together and practiced a lot. It sounded okay so we assembled at about 11pm on New Year's Eve. It was bitterly cold. The snow was around three feet high. Danny the guitarist warned me that the guitar would go out of tune rapidly and so would my accordion so we should get inside as soon as people opened their door. Alan the trumpeter showed us the house of a factory director and dead on midnight we started to play.

We were ushered into the house still playing a popular piece. The house was full of local dignitaries, most of them well intoxicated. One of the women grabbed Alan and began to pull him towards the next room. Another lady started to embrace me and pressed the keys on my accordion. Danny looked at me but we knew that we should stick to our plan and not fall for this pleasant distraction. I observed that the husband of the lady trying to kiss me was getting very embarrassed and that the situation could quickly get out of control. We had a few drinks and were showered with a lot of bank notes which we stuffed into our pockets. We then left, visiting another four houses and ended up with a lot of money!

As well as being a musician, I also wanted to learn how to swim and was persistently trailing the older two neighbours who were swimming across the aforementioned fast-flowing river. They agreed to teach me how to swim and the day after this, we went to the river. As we approached the bank, which was high above the river flow, they simply threw me into the strong current! I went under the water like a stone.

I thought that I was as good as dead. My neighbour Stana, who was four years older than me, grabbed me by the leg and pulled me to the surface. I must have swallowed a lot of water and while I was coughing he held me in the air above his head. He then asked me if I was frightened, to which I replied: "Not any more!"

The first swimming lesson was over and the next day I just followed Stana to the river again and we continued where we had left off the day before. Within two weeks I could swim alone across that deep turbulent choppy river. But in the meantime, a tragedy unconnected to the river was lurking, waiting just around the corner.

8

The Barn, the Bargain and a Bomb

Tony was doing better at school than my other two pupils. A few months later, my friend Miro from next door approached me and mentioned Tony's name. I said: "Yes, what about him?"

"Well", he replied, "I have heard that he has an arsenal of pistols, rifles, machine guns and all sorts of other weaponry at his farm which was left by the retreating Germans after the WWII." I responded that this was all news to me and Tony had never mentioned anything about what was on his farm.

Even then, I was known as a schoolboy who never asked silly questions and didn't gossip. I dismissed the conversation out of hand but just the mention of guns sent a chill down my spine. I concluded with Miro by stating that whatever Tony did or did not have was not my concern, hopefully putting an end to his inquisitiveness.

At the time, not everybody had a TV set or radio in our country. We boys resorted to making our own little listening devices, consisting of bits and pieces of Post Office headphones, crystals, and antennae. It so happened that I needed a new crystal, and who did I ask? None other than Miro.

We haggled over the price, and finally Miro suggested that he could get me a complete radio if I introduced him to Tony. At the time I saw no harm in doing this. All I had to do was get the two together in order to obtain a free radio. The seeds, that would trigger a chain of events leading to disaster,

13

were sown.

A whole week passed before I next visited Tony due to the fact that I skipped a few lessons. His mother was relieved to see me again. During our lesson I explained what had been discussed between me and Miro, who Tony knew despite him not being in his class. I made it clear to Tony that I did not wish to be directly involved in their business, although obtaining my free radio was reliant on their meeting. I also said that he was under no obligation to meet Miro, and that it was not my idea.

Tony wondered how Miro had found out about the arms cache. He sat and stared at me and asked me what he should do. I replied in a cautious tone telling him to forget about the whole thing. I made it clear that he was not indebted to me just because I was his tutor.

A week went by, and with some relief, I didn't see Miro, but Tony wanted to know if I had heard anything from him. I repeated to him that the whole thing should be left dead and buried. He could approach Miro of his own volition but I was out of it. Instead he should concentrate on how to pass his exams.

Nothing occurred for two weeks. Miro came to try and speak to me at my aunt's house, but when I saw him approaching, I simply went through the back door and waited on the terrace until he gave up calling for me. It was March and we still had a lot of snow. Half term was approaching and the whole class was supposed to spend a few days on the ski slopes of Slovenia. I did not want to go.

There was too much going on in my head. I was still avoiding my father which was an added complication as he was well aware of this.

My father began to behave towards me in a more unpleasant manner. While my mother tried to draw me back into the family, my father bickered and verbally abused me at the dinner table. I would avoid this by pretending to go to the toilet, then heading off for my aunty's house.

My mother had confided to my aunt that my father was accusing my mother of being unfaithful, stating that I was illegitimate and did not look like my brother and sister. These accusations had been going on before the gun incident. Despite resembling my father in my later years, my aunt Hanika's words stuck in my mind forever.

During half term there was no need to see Tony and I was busy with my pigeons. I had started with one, but this soon turned into fifty. Despite giving some of them away, the numbers increased.

The neighbours started complaining about them. I needed to solve this problem before the pigeons were shot. Despite winning some cash in competitions, it all went on their food, as a racing pigeon eats about the same as a hen but is not as productive.

Racing pigeons are different from common town pigeons but not when it comes to feeding as they are very loyal to their handler. As for their built-in homing skills, I would say 'the jury is still out'. I decided, that as soon as the half term was over, most of them would have to be given away for breeding.

There was no way I would allow them to come to any harm, since it was I who had unwittingly caused their number to get out of control. Unfortunately, they would have to be kept in cages for the rest of their lives, otherwise they would come back to me which is why racing pigeons have been used many times in history to carry to and fro messages tied to their legs over very long distances.

Soon after half term was over, Miro came to see me at the school playground. I agreed to meet him at the school gates after school. When he appeared, he produced a radio from his school bag. "Why are you showing me this?" I asked, looking into his eyes.

"This is what we agreed on a while ago. Don't you remember?" he replied. I stated that I did remember and presumed that he had been in touch with Tony.

"Yes" he responded nervously. "I am meeting him shortly."

I replied that I didn't want anything to do with all this wheeling and dealing and I got angry with him despite his being more physically formidable than me.

"All right," he said. "I will sell this thing to someone else." I nodded and left.

At my next lesson with Tony, the question popped up about whether I was happy with what he had done.

"What would that be?" I asked, trying to appear absent minded.

"Zdenko," he murmured. "I have done what you asked me to do before the break up of half-term, and Miro will give me a brand new radio in exchange for a few rounds of ammunition which are stored in our barn. After homework is done, I will show you."

It was getting dark, and I wanted to finish what we were doing for the day. When we stepped outside, the snow had begun falling, and soon the air was bursting with countless numbers of little flakes falling on our heads. When we reached the entrance to the barn, Tony produced a torch light and went forward. Inside it was huge and spacious with room for two or three horse carts. The far wall was covered with cobwebs and dry rot. On the wall were shelves that ran from one end to the other, crammed with discarded shoe boxes and all kinds of tools. To my left were bales of hay.

Tony dug into one of them, and produced a small shoe box containing a row of cylindrical objects about three by two inches in size.

"What is that?" I asked. Tony took one in his hand and shone the light on it. "It's an Italian offensive bomb", he said. It did not matter to me whether it was offensive, defensive or inoffensive, it was still a bomb.

I began to question Tony about the machine guns that were supposedly being stored in his barn and within a few moments he dug a machine gun out of another nearby stack of hay. My heart was racing like mad.

"Are there more?" I asked him, hiding my fear. He said there were a lot more. He tried to assure me how safe the arsenal was, but when I told him that in the event of a fire everything would be blown to pieces, he looked at me with disbelief.

I explained to him how I saw with my own eyes a grenade being blown up by a friend of my brother's on one of the tiny river islands, not far from where I dumped my father's pistol a year later, and what a crater it had made.

In those days, there was so much armoury that had been left by the retreating Nazis, every so often there were articles in the daily newspapers about leftover bombs, grenades, cannons and the like. On leaving, I said to Tony that as far as I was concerned, I had seen nothing.

As I walked to my aunt's house, my head was in turmoil and I didn't know what to do. Should I talk to my aunty? Should I betray Tony's confidence? Should I talk to my brother Thomas? I decided to keep quiet, hoping that Miro would not make that little exchange deal, which in all reality wasn't a little deal any more but a big one.

Days passed and Miro did not come to see me. On my next visit to Tony's home, his mother asked me if there was anything unusual happening between her son and me. I said that there was nothing that I knew of, hoping Tony had told her about Miro so allowing me to confess what I knew while giving me the opportunity to warn her of how dangerous the arsenal in the barn was. But she left the kitchen without saying anything.

Tony told me hastily how well he had done in his exams and that he was looking forward to his finals. I remember saying he should tell his mother this and ask her not be too inquisitive towards me. But he wanted me to tell her about the exams since, in his opinion, it was due to my help he had done so well. Eventually Tony went to tell his mum about the exam results. She returned excited and so did his father whom I had met occasionally.

I felt uneasy about all the attention I got. Tony's father insisted that I stay for dinner, which I politely declined. How could I enjoy being at my school mate's house, eating their dinner, while deep down inside, I longed for that to happen with my own family? Again his mum loaded me with some wholesome home-baked bread, ham and farm eggs.

The 'little' deal between Tony and Miro involved a hand grenade instead of a round of ammunition. How would it turn out and what did Miro intend to do with the hand grenade? Had he got any scores to settle? Would he bring that grenade to school and throw it into one of the classrooms?

I had to go and see him. We were talking outside his home for about half an hour. All that Miro wanted to do was to take the hand grenade to a slope not far from where we lived and let it off. To me, the whole thing seemed less dangerous but it reminded me of when The Partisans threw hand grenades into German entrenchments.

There was one thing that Miro asked me to do, to be loyal and present at the exchange of radio and grenade. I would become implicated in the deal but not receive any reward for my mediation.

Miro set the date and time which was for the following week. Tony saw me the next morning at school and said he was agreeable with meeting Miro and would I convey that to him. I also informed Tony that Miro had requested my presence at the exchange. Tony paused and explained that he wished to change the deal and that he would like to activate the hand grenade personally. I told him he couldn't have his cake and eat it.

"It is not that" he said. By this time I was agitated as I did not want to get involved and was getting sick of all the grief. Tony begged me to listed to him.

"All right" I replied "but make it quick".

Tony suggested that if Miro failed to explode the grenade after three attempts then he should have three tries. If he wasn't successful then Miro could make another three attempts. In the event of the grenade not exploding at all, Miro could take it home.

There was a twisted logic in all this madness. Tony was worried that if he handed over the grenade with no qualifications, God knows where it would end. Time was ticking away. I hoped that Miro would change his mind or that Tony would call the deal off.

Meanwhile, I was busy transferring my racing pigeons to a breeder who felt as sorry for them as I did. All the money I received from those sold went on to buy food for the others.

Trouble flared up again between me and my father and I skipped a few classes at school. Finally the day of the exchange arrived - Wednesday, 13th March 1963. Miro came to my aunt's house at about 2pm and we walked together towards the slope near Tony's home where Miro would wait at the deserted German bunker.

I crossed a field towards the main road where Tony lived.

mother that her son was lying on the ground some five hundred yards away and had lost part of his forearm. After that I ran into our house and told my mother what had happened. She said I was to wait there and she rushed to Miro's house.

As both mothers were racing towards the scene of the tragedy, I was beside myself with worry. The traumatic scenario began to reappear in front of my eyes - Miro lying on the ground covered with snow, blood splattered around him; Tony with his hands and blackened face covered in blood. A total nightmare!

Here I was, involved in something I hadn't asked for, and still reeling from the first near tragedy with my father, having to cope with the fact that the grenade could have maimed all of us or even killed Tony, Miro and me.

The reason I had no injuries was that Miro's body had taken most of the shrapnel even though I was standing not far behind him. The second safety feature on that hand grenade was explained to me by one of the army explosives removal team: while we had been trying to shake that grenade off the tree branch, the tiny splint that was holding the pin had fallen off and a mechanism in the grenade had triggered the pin to sink and hit the explosives inside. It had taken fifteen seconds between me handing the grenade over to Miro before it went off.

I still remember finding solace in cuddling my stray cat Jimmy. He followed me everywhere like a dog would. I had to watch him so he would not kill any of my young pigeons but we had a special bond for reasons unknown to me. When I talked to him while he was seemingly sleeping. he would flick his tail at every word I said. My mother told me that he was continuously watching for me and that from the way he behaved, she could tell when I was on my way home. On the day of that tragedy, Jimmy wouldn't leave my side.

But there were still critical and hard times ahead of me!

My mother had told me something out of the blue about her past and told me never to repeat to anyone.

Her words: "Your father had nothing when I met him and the house we lived in was exchanged for the spacious flat I received through a wealthy Jewish family by whom I was employed as an governess. They trusted me more than anybody and I was told that they would be fleeing our town before Hitler's invasion.

On the eve of their departure their children were clinging to my skirt and cried. I was also crying and wanted to join them but they declined fearing for my safety. I promised that I would take care of their possessions till they return.

Two days later I was visited by the secret police who wanted to know where the family were. Of course I didn't know and to this day I still don't know where they went nor where they are. I have tried to find out through their distant families but instead received another visit from the police and had to stop making further inquiries for the sake of our family."

7

Escape from the Border

There I was, just turned fifteen, burdened with the thoughts of how unfortunate I was at my young age to be connected with those two tragic events. The prospect of being interviewed by the police did not bother me since, deep inside, I felt no guilt as such because I had not gained personally from the event. But I did have regrets that my friend Miro had lost half of his arm and had other injuries to his body.

After I was sent home I went to see Miro at the hospital. His mother was there, as was his uncle who knew me. Miro had just been wheeled into the ward next to the chairs where we sat waiting. His mother burst into tears as she had her first glimpse of his bandaged arm which had been amputated from the elbow. He was conscious enough to recognise his mum, his uncle and me. All he said, was: "Zdenko, it was all my fault".

Unfortunately, maybe due to influence from his family, he later tried to partially change the truth about the events leading up to the disaster. We had all been thoroughly interrogated by the police. Tony's parents had been questioned by the anti-terrorist unit to establish whether they had informed the authorities about the arsenal found on their farm. But without Tony's knowledge, they had in fact let the authorities know the moment they moved into the premises. As I mentioned earlier, there were bombs, pistols, grenades and heavy machine guns, as well as cars and motorcycles, found on almost every farm previously occupied by the German army.

It was laid before the High Court judge that due to the work overload of the army disposal unit, there was nobody directly responsible for the tragedy. It was established beyond reasonable doubt that Tony, Miro and I had all had the grenade in our hands at one time or another on that day and that it could have gone off at any time while carrying it around. There was no reason why Tony and I would want to hurt Miro: he was our school friend as well as my neighbour.

Sadly, a few years later, I was told by some of his friends that Miro became a collector of guns and various other artillery shells which are equally dangerous. It confirmed to me that I was only a component in that tragedy. My one hope is that nothing that tragic will happen to him again.

Immediately after Tony's parents' short trial, and the 'not guilty' verdict, I felt a great sense of relief. Unfortunately, a few weeks afterwards, my behaviour began to spiral out of control again. My father wanted me out of the house, and my mother wanted me to remain in the family.

I took most of my belongings and went to live with my aunt Hanika. She was pleased that at least I would be under her roof and that she could keep an eye on me, or so she thought. Her husband began to have doubts about my mental health but I did not have any need for medical help. All I wanted was to go somewhere where nobody knew me.

I still wished to enrol in college to study physics and my marks were good enough to qualify for the entry level at the physics college. Nobody in my circle believed that I would be admitted to the college because of my bad behaviour at school in the past - but I was.

At first, I felt adrift amongst the other students. Yet to my delight, I quickly settled and made friends. They were excited about learning but as my new classmates tossed their backpacks into their parents' cars to head home, I soon realised that there was nobody to pick me up. I didn't even have the bus fare to either return to my aunty or home.

I could not do my homework at home either because of my father's constant interruptions. I quickly came to feel that I might never finish my studies: I was beginning to get behind with my homework; I didn't even have enough money to pay for the college lunches.

It went from bad to worse. The sister of one of my new professors was also a teacher at my old school. He soon pulled me to one side and in a very polite manner warned me that despite the good marks from my old school and the trauma I had suffered, I would not be able to continue without doing all the homework. I knew from that moment on that my fate was sealed.

A month later I quit the college. Of course, I could not go home even if I had wanted to. My uncle became impatient with my state of affairs and attitude towards my future. Within a week I left my aunt's house.

I met some new people in town. Most of them were in a similar situation. I quickly adapted to a new way of life: living on the streets. Every evening, I was forced to find somewhere to stay overnight. I was slowly but surely sinking deeper and deeper into trouble. Many times I had to leave in the middle of the night because the other occupants were involved in thieving, pick pocketing and other criminal activities. I didn't want to go down that route for anything.

I resorted to cinema ticket touting, which of course was illegal, but at least it wasn't a criminal offence.

There was an open air swimming complex with three different sized pools just on the outskirts of my town. Among the group that I swam with, there was some kind of initiation ritual whereby I would only be accepted if I had the courage to dive into the pool from the height of some thirty-three feet.

I started to dive from the height of fifteen feet and then from twenty feet and after an hour I was ready to dive from the highest point. Because there had been accidents before, the management had blocked the entry steps leading to the top of that particular spring board. There was a pool lifeguard always on duty and only qualified divers were allowed to use the highest diving point. What was funny about this was the fact that there was hardly anybody qualified enough to dive from the top!

My group leader of ten youths, mainly older than me, was watching when the pool guard went to collect his lunch from the restaurant about a hundred feet away. When the moment came, the signal was given by my group leader to go ahead. I jumped over a small fence which separated the lower and highest part of the ramp and rushed up the remaining twenty steps to reach the top. The rest of the group and some onlookers were all standing and watching me around the pool. I had no fear except that the wind might change the momentum of my body and I would land on my belly instead of head down, or worse, damage my spine.

I paused for a moment and then thrust myself outwards - I was in the air and falling fast. It all happened in the blink of an eye. It must have been a split second or so as I stretched my arms in front of my head to protect it from the impact of my body hitting the surface of the water.

That was not the end of it though. People were applauding but I had to leave the pool as quickly as possible because I was breaking the rules of the complex and if found I would be barred. After a few minutes I melted into the crowds around one of the pools and was congratulated by my group leader whose name was Karl. I was accepted by his group - the youngest and smallest of them all at the time.

Meanwhile, my poor mother was wandering the streets of our town asking people whether they knew me or had seen me lately. However, she was trying to turn back the clock because my life was at the point of no return. I was beginning to think about the possibility of illegally crossing the heavily protected international border and fleeing to Austria.

At that time, I was only hatching the idea. I asked my newly gained friends what happened if a man succeeded in doing this and what went on to happen afterwards. The things I found out were all a bit sketchy. Apparently, it was down to someone's physical strength. Countries like Sweden were looking for strong young men to work in their forest industry and coal mines. I would be an unlikely candidate since I weighed some six stone and my height was only five foot four! The only possibility for me being allowed to remain in any

Western country was if I could cross Austrian territory undetected and reach West Germany (as it then was).

It wasn't long before I was approached by two slightly older youths. They briefly asked me if may name was Zdenko and if I spoke some German or English. My reply was yes, that I did, and how could I help them.

At that time, it was a craze to write to different car manufacturers in the West and enquire about their brochures and badges. I had helped many of my friends to write those letters in German and English. The manufacturers did not realise that we were only interested in their badges.

The taller of the two, whose name was Ivor, asked me if I could meet them at a guest house that was in one of the seedy areas of town. By then, I was not afraid of anything and gave them a time when it would be convenient.

One of my new mates from town who happened to be passing by and knew the pair advised me to be extremely careful with them - allegedly both of Milo's brothers were serving a long prison sentence for armed robbery - but I did not want to break a promise, and I could learn something new in the process. I also needed to know some of the 'heavy boys' in town in case I got bullied.

I arrived on time. Ivor and his accomplice, by the name of Milo, were already at the bar of the strange-looking guest house. The juke-box was blaring at its maximum, so I immediately suggested that we go to the garden terrace where we could hear each other properly.

As we sat down at the table, Ivor mumbled something like:

"I never beat around the bush" and wanted to come straight to the point. They were looking for someone who could help them to abscond from the Yugoslav State very soon. They would have some of Ivor's relatives on the Austrian side waiting for us. I asked what was in it for me and what would my role be. Ivor explained that as we would be very near the border marked with granite stones, I should be talking aloud about anything as long it was in German. There was no 'no man's land'. The Yugoslav border guards in all probability wouldn't speak or understand any German, and therefore it would be logical to presume that they would think we were a group of Austrians.

Ivor had a hand-drawn map of the spot where we would make the crossing but although theoretically we would already be on Austrian soil, we would still be walking next to the border control military posts on the Yugoslav side. That was the point where my knowledge of the German language would come into play.

It was a cleverly worked out plan, since I knew that somewhere very close was the river which acted as the border. There was a bridge where Ivor's relatives would wait for us. The exact border line was somewhere in the middle of that river. I knew how Austrians dressed since a lot of Austrians came to our town to do their shopping because their currency was very strong.

By law, any able-bodied man between eighteen and fifty-five years of age was listed as a potential conscript to do national service.

Escape from the Border

The length of service ranged between eighteen and twenty-four months. For this reason, many young men tried to avoid serving in the army and resorted to fleeing the country. Ivor and Milo were two of them. I, on the other hand, still had eighteen months left before the authorities would serve me with a notice to enlist but I had no choice other than to flee with no home, no college to go to, and nobody from my family who dared help me get a job in any of more than twenty factories in a small town like Maribor despite the fact there were people in the wide circle of my family who were quite high ranking board members in various concerns. I had been told by my aunty Hanika, who knew them all and had tried to make them aware that I needed help, that they 'would not touch me with a barge pole'! Of course I sensed the influence of my father who said that I was no good for anything.

What I was going to do was not a desertion but an act of desperation. There were no reasons for me to be patriotic about my country of birth at all.

Since I understood spoken and written German, reading the various articles that were somehow filtered through the state censorship didn't help. I realised more than any of my friends that Yugoslavia was an artificial state and that it was doomed to fail (which in the end it did). I didn't ask 'what my country could do for me', instead I wanted to help myself, but I was going around in circles. With no fixed address I couldn't apply for any of the jobs going. Those two older boys at least had a home to go to. I am sure they were loved by their parents.

There was one thing that bugged me. I asked Ivor: "Why risk being recognised by the border patrol as not being Austrian at all? Instead, why could we not simply board a local bus in the direction of the border crossing, and get off some 200 yards before. I could still be talking in German and act as an Austrian".

The one problem with this plan was that they did not possess any smart clothing similar to the clothes Austrians wore. The other passengers would quickly realise that we looked nothing like Austrians. Had I been on my own, I was confident that I could have been passed off as Austrian but most of the bus passengers would be local and as soon as we left the bus, they would inform on us. Besides, if we had to change the marked route and go across the river, the two could not swim well enough to cross the fast flowing water to reach the Austrian side.

For myself, I saw no problem in swimming across that river. As I mentioned earlier I had swum across the strong river currents close to my home countless times. And as for my clothes, I had earned plenty of money by touting the cinema tickets three times a week with all the proceeds going on my upkeep and what I wore.

My ticket-touting enterprise was big enough to take on two helpers. I would explain the pitfalls to them and who to bribe in order to ply the trade without any hindrance. I was lucky too as I happened to be a neighbour of three much older and experienced ticket touts. They even bribed the woman who worked at the ticket office. Sometimes, I didn't have to join the queue and buy the tickets for a particular show. All I had to do was to pay a commission to my three neighbours. At the same time, I had protection from the competition. I was shown how to spot any police presence, and how to bribe them too if necessary.

Ivor and Milo knew what I was doing, and ironically they respected me for that. But as far as I was concerned it was the wrong sort of respect. I would much rather have had a home and finished my studies.

All that was left was to set the date and time when we would carry out the journey to the West. Once we all agreed on the date, my remaining question was that after a successful crossing, how long would Ivor's family members wait for us in case of any delay and was there another set time when they would return to the pick-up point on the Austrian side? I insisted that once over the border I should be driven to the nearest railway station where I could change my clothes and from there I would make my own way towards West Germany. Ivor agreed. I also demanded that in the weeks ahead, we should meet at least once before the border crossing attempt. We had to work out in detail what we would take with us and what was needed for the journey.

About a week afterwards we met up again. Ivor had a list which had been handed to him via his family network who were already in Austria. The instructions were very clear. We had to try and travel by daylight towards the border crossing post by local bus without any luggage or shopping bags so as not to arouse any suspicion. By law, all the local inhabitants were compelled to inform the police of any suspicious passengers who were travelling in that direction. Also, all the farmers who lived nearby had to comply with that law. We were therefore to have only a few items on us, and a small carrier bag in which were to be some bread, a few tomatoes, sliced salami and some tinned fish. We were not to stuff our pockets with anything that would cause a visible bulge on our bodies.

There were only three days left before our departure. In the meantime, I went to see my mother who was relieved to see me. I was well dressed and not in bad shape. She didn't ask me any questions apart from my address so that she could come and see me more often. But I didn't want her to worry about my various temporary places of abode and the style of my life. As I left, she tried to give me some money which I refused to take.

I had to go and see my aunty Hanika as well. When my aunt saw me, she ran towards me with tears in her eyes. She looked very upset and asked me why I had not been to visit her. I didn't want to mention the conversation that I had had with her husband a few weeks earlier regarding my future. After all, I wasn't his immediate family, and he was simply worried about me staying at his house without any income on my part. I understood his concern.

My aunty said that my father was quite pleased not to have me around so that he could devote more time to my brother Thomas whom he doted on. Aunty just couldn't understand that I had mentally left all that behind me. She asked me to come back again and try to enrol at a different college. She also knew one of the teachers at the music college where I could enrol with my musical talent: as well as the accordion, I also played the piano. She would support me in every way.

When she saw the look on my face, I could see that finally she had realised that all her persuasion was in vain and I wanted to choose my own destiny. I didn't tell her about my forthcoming journey and the hope for a new life in the West. I turned down her invitation to have lunch mainly because I hadn't eaten anything at my mum's and did not want to show favouritism. I played a bit with her dog Astra who wouldn't leave my side as if she sensed that she wouldn't see me for a good while.

After half an hour I hastily said goodbye to her and made my way towards the town. I called at the guest house where Ivor and Milo were most probably having a last drink, being as it was their 'local'. To my surprise they were seemingly in deep conversation and completely sober. It gave me some assurance that they were serious about our escape to Austria.

As soon as they noticed my presence, they both stood up and proclaimed: "This is our man!" They greeted me as if we had known each other for ages. My aunty had told me as I was leaving that she felt pains in her bones which surely meant bad weather was approaching. After my explanation about how bad weather could endanger our mission it was decided that we bring the departure forward to the next day. The following day we assembled at the bus station and boarded the bus which would take us to the village a few miles before the border. I casually checked if there were any policemen or border guards disguised as passengers. The bus was full of people and I didn't see any sign that the passengers were suspicious of us.

Milo and Ivor were dressed in their best suits, clean shaven and both had a paper carrier bag under their arm with the bread loaves sticking out in the open. I knew the area well and began to count the stops. After about fifteen stops Ivor gave me a wink to say that the next stop was ours.

As we stepped out of the bus, there was a Yugoslav army border control car passing by on the opposite side of the road going in the direction of our town. As soon as the car went round the corner we jumped into the corn field. We stopped and listened to hear if there was anybody in that cornfield who could immediately report us to the police. All we heard was singing coming from the potato field a hundred yards away.

We began to discuss what to do next in whispering voices. It was five o'clock in the afternoon and I calculated that we would have to wait for at least an hour before we could move again. We decided to have a late lunch. The soil was moist so we made cushions out of the corn leaves. We unwrapped our paper shopping bags and began to eat what we had. Milo had six tins of sardines in his pockets and gave me and Ivor one each, saying that he had 'nicked' the remaining four from the store at the bus station. I immediately pointed out that he could have been stopped for shoplifting and jeopardised the whole mission. I could see that Ivor was under Milo's influence since he said nothing. I saw that his left pocket was still bulging and asked Milo if he had any more of the stuff he had nicked from that store. He then pulled out a pistol and said that it was his property.

There I was trying my luck in the West in the company of an armed shoplifter and possible bank robber! All sorts of thoughts were racing through my mind. What could be a way out of the situation?

I decided that I would pull out of our expedition and make my way back to Maribor. Ivor pleaded with me that they would be lost without me and that I should leave it to him to talk to Milo. But Milo wouldn't listen to Ivor at all. Of course, it had been playing on my mind that perhaps Milo would use his gun to threaten me at the moment I became stubborn. I had been threatened before and had always been able to turn the situation around. There was also the thought that it was too late go back and I would simply have to deal with Milo whatever might happen.

I had to change my tactics. I bluntly told him that the way he was holding the gun showed me that he had probably never fired that gun or any other, and that he would miss his target even if it was two or three feet away. I made him listen to me for a few more minutes.

"You", I said quietly, "haven't a clue how many arms I've handled in the past. From hand grenades, canons, shotguns, machine guns etc. - the whole works! And if you think I am afraid of you because you have a gun, you are mistaken. And besides, I am not going anywhere if you don't leave this weapon behind."

I added that although he was older, it meant nothing to me. Milo realised that he was facing someone who dared to talk to him as if he were a school boy and had no fear! I also added the possible scenario of how he would be imprisoned in Austria if he were found in possession of a gun. I asked Ivor if he too had some kind of weapon on him. Ivor showed his pocket knife and said that he only took that knife with him because it had a small compass mounted on the grip end.

One by one, the farmers' voices faded into the distance. Milo gave me a look of defeat after I said: "It's all settled then". It was only at that point I realised that he was very strong and could be dangerous. What Ivor and Milo didn't know was the fact that I knew they were going to use me and in return I was using them as physical protection should the need arise. After a successful crossing I was going to ditch Milo anyway; but for the moment he could be handy in case we were intercepted by any local gangs preying on people they found crossing the border illegally. Most of those unfortunate people were robbed at gunpoint and one of those gangs could be in the field right at that moment!

Milo eventually threw his gun into the bushes surrounding the field. The farmers' voices were now out of earshot. The sun had almost disappeared behind the hills. The new moon was rising on our right. It was time to go.

According to Ivor's hand drawn map, we were to march in the direction of north. As we crossed a strip of land with a potato crop, I quietly asked Ivor to show me his knife with the compass and compared it with the map and the direction in which we were going. I pointed out to Ivor that the compass was giving us a false reading. The needle was pointing towards east and we were supposed to be heading north. I told Ivor that the compass had probably demagnetised itself because of the steel casing it was in. I asked them both if they knew exactly where we were.

They were both telling me positions which were wrong so I showed them how to navigate with only the moon as a navigation aid. (I learned that as a Scout and also while observing my pigeons.) They followed my footsteps from then on.

After marching for about an hour, we came across a white painted square board that was fixed to a concrete pole about eight feet above the ground, just before a thinning part of the woodland ahead of us. Milo wanted to use his lighter to see what was written on it. I was able at the last moment to stop him lighting the damned lighter! I realised that he was becoming a liability. I told Ivor that we would wait for the moon to appear through the newly formed clouds, and then see what it said. After a minute or so, the moon was piercing between the cloud and Ivor lifted me off the ground so that I could see what the board was saying. It read:

HALT! YOU ARE ABOUT TO ENTER A MILITARY
CONTROLLED BORDER ZONE.
The personnel are under orders to shoot on sight

LEAVE THIS AREA IMMEDIATELY.

At the bottom was another smaller text in Serbo-Croat. There were two skulls with crossbones painted in red on each side of the warning board. We looked at each other and continued walking. Shortly after, we heard a rumbling noise coming from the distance.

It meant rain and also the loss of orientation. The moon was our only salvation and without it, in a very short space of time we would be hopelessly lost.

I stopped again and suggested in a whispered voice that we abort the crossing. Ivor wanted to press ahead and so did Milo. I maintained that there was no chance of knowing which direction we were heading in once the clouds covered the moon. Ivor sat down on what looked like a tree stump. I said that we were about a yard away from Austria. Milo became excited but Ivor and I had a gut feeling that it wouldn't be that easy. From where we stood, still facing north, the writing on the border marking stone had the letters:

SFRJ (meaning Yugoslavia)

and that side was facing in the direction towards east. At my last glimpse of the moon's position, we were supposed to continue straight ahead, but the arrow on the granite marker pointed east. We decided to follow the direction towards east.

Then we felt the first raindrops, followed by lightning and at each lightning flash, we could see the terrain ahead. I kept going in a straight line as much as possible despite the undergrowth that was slowing down our progress. When we reached the next border marker stone, the arrow on it was pointing south! How was this possible if I had strictly walked in a straight line? With my heart thumping, I came to realise that the border line was running in a zigzag fashion, designed to confuse people who were trying to escape from Yugoslavia. I looked up between the tree tops to see if the moon was anywhere to be seen.

By now, the rain had become heavy and quickly turned into a downpour. The lightning was becoming more intense and we were totally drenched. What looked to be a few hour's journey had become a six-hour march without knowing where we were and without any proper clothing. The moon was hidden behind the thick clouds. All I could see was a dim light spot in between them, but it was at the wrong place. It came through the clouds behind us!

I suggested that we turn around and try again in the next few days. Ivor and Milo once more were having none of this. At the same time, I did not want to abandon them. We continued to fight our way through the rough terrain but I presumed that we were just going in circles. Suddenly, in a flash of lightning, I spotted a thin glistening wire mesh which appeared like a giant spider web blocking our way. Milo stretched his hand to brush aside the obstacle and I was too late to stop him. I sensed that it might be some kind of an alarm system, and by touching those wires the border guards would receive the signal that somebody was trying to cross the border line.

In an instant, there a tremendous firework display above our heads. There were bits of still burning fireworks

coast. As for me, my luck had run out. I was declared a clandestine to be returned to Yugoslavia together with Milo, who was stupidly found to be in possession of another small gun. I didn't want anything more to do with him.

After two weeks the police bus took about twenty of us, all of whom had been refused asylum, back to Yugoslavia and straight to the prison of my home town. The prison staff immediately separated me from the older detainees because of my age but also because I hadn't committed a crime as such. I was just short of my sixteenth birthday. The judge sentenced me to two months youth custody in the prison I was already in.

I expected to be humiliated and manhandled by prison officers but this turned out not to be the case and I was offered a work placement at the town's soap factory. When I entered the factory under the watchful eye of a prison officer, the foreman, also a prisoner whose name was Rony, was waiting for me. He recognised me. Ironically he and his family had just moved into one of the barracks a few hundred yards away from our house.

When we were left alone, Rony scolded me and told me how from now on, my life would be changed for ever. I would have a criminal record and would be labelled as an enemy of the state. "Nobody will employ you," he added.

I told him that it wouldn't be long before I got a passport and left the country again. "Yeah, that is what you think," said Rony and laughed. What he meant was that a person with a criminal record, and especially one with a history of being an opponent to Tito's regime, was not allowed to apply for a passport. I was confident however that I would somehow be able to overcome this obstacle. Of course, I had to finish the remaining six weeks of my sentence and not get involved in any trouble in the prison itself which was very difficult. Fights would erupt on a daily basis and I had to remain neutral amongst fifteen of us, all in one cell. I also learned that I wouldn't have a criminal record after all since I was classed as a juvenile. Nevertheless, I wouldn't be able to obtain a valid passport.

The whole episode of my imprisonment was wrought with one difficulty. Despite all of Rony's lecturing, he himself couldn't stay on the straight and narrow. He was delivering stolen bags of washing powder to private laundries which was not above board and, as I had to countersign all the delivery notes, I was obviously committing a theft.

After two weeks I confronted Rony and told him that I did not want to take part in his activities despite his offer that he pay me for doing so. I asked the prison officer who was in charge of me to be sent to another department. I didn't tell him the reason. Rony appreciated the fact I didn't tip him off and in exchange for my services supplied me with cigarettes and even some brandy on regular basis. He even seemed to have some influence over the guards which made sense as to why was he able to do the pilfering. Most probably they turned a blind eye and benefited from it. But I knew that one day they would be found out and they were. A year later there were rumours that Rony and some prison officers were convicted of theft and punished with prison sentences.

Rony's new sentence was simply added on. I was glad that I had been strong enough to resist the temptation to accept Rony's offer. My future vision was very different from his. I was to be released nine days early but only after my parents had signed some forms because I was a minor.

On the day of my release, when he saw me, my father began to swear and yell at me as to how I dared bring the good name of the family into disrepute. The prison governor warned him that he did not approve of this outburst and that I should be taken home, recognising the possibility that maybe his behaviour towards me was partly to blame for my misfortune.

As we came to a halt at the crossroads, I quickly jumped out of the car and made my way back to the town thinking how dare he have the audacity to mention the word 'disrepute' when it was him to blame for my behaviour in the first place!

I must admit that he was unaware I had intercepted all our mail that included the court correspondence regarding his case which had been nearly two years before. He got off very lightly.

I soon met up again with my fraternity, organised a new ring of future assistants and before I knew it, I was back to my old self. The ticket touting was my sole source of income, and other touts quickly became aware of my harrowing experience and my short spell in prison.

Apparently they had been told by Milo's brother that he had stayed in prison for committing a robbery a few weeks before our botched border crossing attempt. In a way they paid me homage, but I was determined not to end up in prison ever again.

I learned that my father had been offered the opportunity of paying a fine so I would not have had to serve that short prison spell. Deep down I knew that the lifestyle I was living was only a temporary solution. I was planning to bribe someone at the passport office to issue me with a passport or any travel documents. After a few weeks I had enough cash to do that.

The passport cost about a hundred and twenty pounds in today's money. It was a lot but, with the help of my mother and aunty Hanika, I finally managed to get the money together. The people that promised the passport were in no doubt that if it was not forthcoming, I would want my money back. They knew how easy it would be for me to take revenge: although I had never threatened anyone, they all knew that I was not a person to be messed with. I did not like that perception of me but to stay alive on the streets, it was necessary to keep on top of events and potential bullying. I had taken some training and karate lessons just to be able to defend myself.

The passport was handed to me within two weeks and all I could think of was to plan my journey back to the West, only this time with a passport. I checked all the details that were written in the passport and compared them to another passport and it seemed to be alright. I said farewell to only a few of the people that I trusted and said goodbye to my mother and aunty. They finally accepted that there was no hope and future for me in the country of my birth.

I boarded the train which would take me to the first town in Austria. I was advised to buy a return ticket and have some money on me. I was alone in the train compartment when the Yugoslavian border control entered and asked me to produce my passport. They looked at it, asked me a few questions and left the compartment. I did not show any fear, but I had butterflies in my stomach.

Soon afterwards the Austrian border control entered my compartment and they too asked me some questions, mainly if I had enough money to support myself for the length of my stay in their country. After they left though, I was a bit nervous, so I lit a cigarette and felt more uplifted.

I knew that there was a note somewhere in the Austrian immigration files which prohibited me from obtaining a work visa for two years since I had broken the country's law with my illegal entry four months earlier. I was aiming to go to Switzerland and find work and then return to Yugoslavia and wait for my visa to be issued at the Swiss Embassy in Zagreb. I calculated that there wouldn't be enough money to do all that but I stuck to the motto 'nothing ventured nothing gained'.

As I reached the town of Graz, I switched to the train going towards Salzburg some three hundred and fifty miles away. I had no ticket and was hoping that the ticket collector would not spot me on the crowded train. I was lucky and arrived unhindered at Salzburg main train station late that night. It was minus twenty degrees Celsius.

There were a few people standing at the stands and kiosks

eating their snacks and drinking their coffee. I approached a small group of two men and a woman and asked them in broken Italian if they knew a place or a hotel that was not expensive. They replied in Serbo-Croat that they did know of such a place. After I confirmed that I came from the same country as them, we talked about their stay in Austria and made our way towards the tram stop just a stone's throw away from the railway station. The woman was not married to either of the men she was with and made a few passes at me saying how much she liked me and so on. They were actually taking me to their place for the night! But all I could think of was a warm bed where I could put my head down.

We finally reached our destination. The place where they lived was some sort of communal dormitory separated by curtains made of a dark and heavy material. I was shown a double bed, shared washing facilities and the toilets. I couldn't be bothered to wash myself and fell asleep straight away.

The woman, whose name was Sara, woke me up the next morning and, while I washed myself, cooked us breakfast. Her companions left early that morning for work. She was a very pretty woman in her thirties and came on to me really heavily. I explained to her that I was in no state to satisfy her needs. I felt obliged to tell her a few details about my troubled life and she understood but insisted that I stay a bit longer. She said that there were plenty of vacancies for trainee waiters at the restaurant where she worked and that she would talk to her manager and ask him to take me on.

I politely thanked her for her offer but declined it due to the fact my illegal presence in Austria might get her into trouble. I asked her how much I owed her for my short stay, to which she replied that there was nothing to pay and how sorry she was for me. She even offered me some money. There was no way that I would accept anything from her but I left with the promise to at least write to her about how I got on in Switzerland. To this day, I still think of her and her kindness often.

Back at the Salzburg main railway station, I was trying my luck again. After a few hours of watching and observing the trains leaving in the direction of Zurich in Switzerland, I plucked up my courage. Having nothing to lose, I caught the next train bound for Zurich.

It was Christmas time and the train was full. Again, for some unknown reason the ticket collector didn't ask me for my ticket. After a seven-hour journey, the train approached the Swiss border. The locomotives were changed and Swiss Customs began their round. When one of the customs officers asked me about my passport I began to look for it. I knew that I had had it on me when I boarded the train. They turned their attention to the rest of the passengers who were standing nearby while I went to look for it in my little holdall. A Swiss ticket collector saw me searching in my holdall for it but left me alone.

Finally I found it in my back pocket. The customs officers returned and I showed it to them with a great relief. I was asked if I had any cigarettes or spirits in my luggage. I showed them what I had in the holdall. They finally asked me how much money I had on me. I had in total about one hundred and fifty Swiss francs. I also told them that my visit would be no longer than three days and that I would stay at the Swiss YMCA as a bed for the night didn't cost more than two Francs. When asked about the train ticket, I pretended once again to start searching my suitcase. They thought it was funny and left me alone. Phew! I counted my lucky stars once more. Had they found out that I had no ticket, I would have been in big trouble and almost certainly thrown out of the country. I told myself that there must be someone watching over me. I said a prayer and fell asleep.

I was woken by a train guard. He asked me my destination because we had arrived at Zurich and the train had terminated there. Luckily he didn't ask me about my ticket. Unlike some other countries there were no exit barriers. 'So far, so good' I thought. I wanted to push ahead and reach the town of Lucerne before nightfall. I had purposely chosen Lucerne because the largest Swiss hotel employment agency was there.

I took a local bus which according to my Swiss road map would take me in the direction of a motorway leading to my destination. I walked for another two miles, intending to hitch-hike towards Lucerne. Fortune was again on my side since the very first car immediately stopped. It was a lady driver. She spoke German and French and her name was Else. She was twice my age and very beautiful.

I found the way she spoke about her life experiences

hilarious. The time was passing very fast. She asked me where I was going to stay in Lucerne and I told her that I would find a youth hostel and that if necessary, I would have a nap at the railway station. As we were approaching Lucerne, she invited me to her house where she said I could have a rest and the next morning she would take me to the employment agency. She said that I was a very interesting person to listen to.

Her house was beautiful. For the first time in my life I saw a place full of expensive furniture and ornaments. At that time, I didn't have a clue what real antiques looked like but everything suited the place perfectly. Looking at her grand piano and the rest of her furniture and ornaments, I realised it must have all cost a small fortune.

Back in my home town of Maribor I had joined a small group of musically-minded people and every week I was taught the piano at a local theatre. The lessons were free. Even then I knew something about the masters of classical music. My mates were always laughing and giggling about my 'strange musical tastes' because to them the Beatles and the Rolling Stones were 'in'. They started to call me 'The Pianist'.

I asked Else if I could have a shower. After that I was going to ask her about her grand piano. I still remember the name of it: it was a Boesendorfer and it was just beautiful. She showed me where the bathroom was and told me to give her a shout when I had finished. When I came out of the shower I couldn't see where my trousers, shirt and underwear were. Suddenly the bathroom door opened slightly and all I could see was her arm stretching through the door holding a different shirt, pair of trousers and underwear. As I took the fresh clothing from her hand she closed the door again and asked me what drink I preferred. I said that I drank anything.

When I came downstairs she was holding a glass of brandy in her hand and asked me if it was enough for an aperitif.

"The dinner is in the oven as well and it will be ready in about an hour" she said. At the same time, she commented how well the shirt and the trousers looked on me.

I could tell that the garments were made of wool and the shirt felt like silk. I then went straight for the piano and asked her if she could play. She said that the piano belonged to her daughter and that she could only play with two fingers. I asked her if I could open the heavy cover and see the works inside. I touched the strings and my hairs were standing up on my back! She asked me if I played the piano and I answered that all I knew were a few notes.

I tried a few keys and some chords and I could see her eyes opening wide. I started to play one of Bellini's arias, Casta Diva. She looked at me as if to say 'wow'. I played another piece and she just stood there and listened. She then invited me to sit down on the couch and asked me if I was actually a music student and not simply a young man looking for just any kind of work in Switzerland. She said that my demeanour and the way I spoke to her in broken German told her that I wasn't only an adventurous young man. She complimented me on my performance and blurted out presumptuously that none of her previous boyfriends had had any musical talents. I jokingly said that I wasn't her boyfriend but a toy boy.

58

She just laughed.

She started to ask me questions about myself and I told her how my life was wrought with tragedies and full of bad memories and I would rather not go into detail about it. With that, Else propped herself on the couch and began to insist that I at least tell her a part of my life story. The brandy was taking its effect and I thought to myself 'to hell with it and go with the flow'.

The more I told her, the more she asked me about the details. After a few minutes she had tears in her eyes and just looked at me with bewilderment. She took me in her arms and kept saying: "Oh! Poor you, Poor you!"

I told her that I didn't want her to be sorry for me - all of that was behind me now - and that I was sad that she was upset about what had happened to me in the past. I was offered another glass of Swiss plum brandy. Else wanted to hear more but I said that enough had been said and that I didn't need pity from anybody. She said that I should stay with her for a while and that she would help me to publish a book about my life and also enrol me at one of the Swiss music colleges. She had just finished a relationship with her boyfriend. The way she spoke about him revealed that there was no love lost between them.

I told her that my destiny wasn't to live a life on the back of an older woman. I also tried to explain that it just wouldn't work: her, with a property then worth hundreds of thousands of Francs, having a quite good looking young man living off her. My response was that it was out of the question.

After that I tried in my broken German to crack a few jokes, just to move on to a different subject but she went quiet. I asked her if I had said anything to offend her to which she replied that she felt very lonely and had never found the right man - she always attracted the wrong one. I told her that she was beautiful and that one day she would find the man of her dreams. She responded that she had never had a boyfriend who was sophisticated enough.

The dinner was nearly ready and after we finished, I helped her to load the dishwasher although I had never seen one before. I felt courageous enough to speak to her in French as well. I wasn't trying to impress her but wanted to show her that she wouldn't have to be ashamed of me in front of her friends should we meet again some day. We retreated to the huge leather sofa and the way she leaned on me as we sat together told me she wanted to keep me there as long as possible, even if she had to seduce me - which she did. Her one comment was that she had never met a guy like me before. Life is full of surprises!

The next morning, she rang the agency and we were told to come and see them at three o'clock. She then took me to a couple of shops and tried to buy me a suit, shoes, etc. I politely turned down her offer. She was very upset because in her mind, here was a young man with almost nothing who didn't want her help. I simply didn't want to end up as her toy boy. But I did agree that we would take my clothes to the dry cleaners and she could pay for that and nothing more. I needed to be presentable at my possible interview with the employment agency. It was so funny because the more I didn't want anything, the more she wanted to shower me with presents. I retained my self respect and pride.

Else drove a very expensive sports car in which she took me for lunch at, of course, one of the best restaurants in town. She introduced me to the proprietor of the restaurant and I overheard him saying to her in a joking manner that I was "the best" so far.

During our lunch I tried to find out something more about her. She told me how she'd divorced her husband who was cheating on her and how he was trying to steal her inheritance money. Her last boyfriend was no different and she was glad to finish their relationship.   Apparently she was born into a wealthy family of watchmakers in Basle. Throughout the lunch she spoke about how she wanted to find me a job in one of her family's factories and that I should abandon the search for any alternative position since I would be working for her family.

Out of honesty, I told her that it wouldn't work. I tried to explain that they would ask her where she met me and would probably laugh behind her back knowing that I was simply too young for her.

"Look," I said. "You are in your late thirties and you mean well but what about when I want to find a girlfriend my own age? What will happen ten years from now?"

I politely asked her to consider that. I also added that after all, I was just a young hitch-hiker and although my manners were impeccable, I was also only human with my own faults.

A Crime of Passion

She gave me a forlorn look which told me that I was right. I also thanked her for trying to talk to the owner of the restaurant about employing me. I felt he might have taken me on there and then. I continued saying that we hardly knew each other and we should leave things as they were and that in the future we would still be friends and who knew? Maybe one day I could take up her offer to work for her family. I ended the subject by saying that I wanted to try to make something of my life on my own first. Then I reminded Else that we had to be at the employment agency at three o'clock.

When we arrived, we were told that they had secured a vacancy for me at one of the top hotels in the famous St. Moritz and gave me a contract of employment to sign. The agency took a risk and paid for my return rail ticket which was waiting for me at the railway station, giving me two hundred and fifty Francs on account. I was over the moon and Else was also thrilled to see me happy but she still kept saying that I needn't go and that she would take care of me. She tried to assure me that she and her family had friends in Swiss 'high places' but I kept telling her that it would be me, on my own, who would achieve something. She wanted to give me a wad of Swiss banknotes but I refused. However, I suggested that I could take up piano lessons in one of the Swiss music schools and she could pay for my first five lessons. We said our goodbyes and after I took what little belongings I had from the boot of her car, she got out with tears in her eyes to say goodbye.

I took the first train as advised and returned to Maribor

with one exception to my trip out. This time I had a valid ticket! When I reached Salzburg again I wanted to check if my jacket had been cleaned properly and I noticed there was an envelope with Else's handwriting on it which contained one hundred and fifty Swiss francs.

It took about two months for the visa to be issued at the Swiss Embassy in Zagreb (Croatia). I didn't tell anybody about my arrangements apart from my mother and aunty Hanika in case somebody might 'squeal on me'. All the newly-gained friends in my home town wondered where I had been. I didn't want to tell them anything.

On the day my passport's arrival along with a stamped Swiss working permit, I got very drunk and nobody knew why. I bought a few rounds of drinks and went to sleep at my friend's place.

The next day I went to see my mother and aunty to say goodbye for the fourth time except now I felt very confident about my future. I stepped onto the train with an assuredness I had not felt before. After all, I had a return ticket direct to Lucerne and once there, a hotel taxi would take me up the Swiss mountains to the place where I could commence work as assistant to the concierge.

Everything was fine with the journey, just as I imagined it would be. The hotel had a hundred and fifty rooms and suites. On my arrival, the hotel in-house tailor took my measurements and I felt happy as never before. I quickly learned how to operate the switchboard, how to book a tour for the guests, organise the arrivals and departures and many other things that I picked up as I went along. To this day, I believe that Else had some influence on the employment agency which found me that placement as swiftly as they did.

The concierge called me Cenko. I asked why Cenko and not Zdenko to which he replied that there was a similar word in Italian, 'cento', which meant a percentage of something. I would be getting a tenth of the gratuities that were shared between the reception staff. We were on low fixed wages, but the bulk of our wages consisted of service charges which were at fifteen percent. I didn't think it was bad for a young man like me.

After two weeks, I decided to send Else a postcard telling her how good I felt. I had her phone number but preferred to write to her in case she had found a new partner. I enclosed the phone number of my hotel and waited for her reply. A few days passed and while covering the afternoon shift, I answered a phone call which came from the police headquarters in Zurich. The person at the other end asked me if I knew how to contact Mr Zdenko Ornig.

My first thought was that they had found out something about my passport. But my passport was legitimate. I listened very attentively to what the person, presumably a police officer, at the other end of the line was telling me. He continued to say slowly, so I was able to understand, that I was not being treated as a suspect. Nevertheless, he would have to talk to me in person. He put me at ease and said that he would not come to the hotel and compromise my reputation but would meet me at the local police station near the hotel that evening and that I should bring my passport along as well. He repeated again that I shouldn't worry since the danger was over.

"What danger?" I gasped. He rang off with the words that he would see me that evening at seven o'clock. I sensed something sinister must have happened since the police could not get the number from anyone but Else. I tried to ring her number but the operator said that the number was unobtainable.

As I stepped into the building at exactly seven o'clock there was a Swiss CID man in plain clothes. Next to him stood a young woman in her twenties dressed in a long black coat. She resembled Else very much. The detective introduced himself as Herr Kolbe and the young lady as Fraulein Stahl. We were ushered into the next available room and a tray of coffee was brought into the room almost immediately. The young lady asked me if my name was Zdenko and had I met Frau Else Stahl about four months previously. "Yes" I said. She broke down in tears.

The detective asked me for my passport and he quickly went into the next room with it. I could see through the window into the next room how the CID and two other men, also in plain clothes, were poring over my passport. They were typing my details into what looked like a telex machine.

Fraulein Stahl was beginning to talk to me and noticed that I was very nervous. She said that there was nothing to be afraid of and that I was innocent as far as she was concerned. She had spoken to her mother Else the very same evening after I left her in Lucerne.

The CID then returned with my passport and told me that he had to go through the formality of identifying me to eliminate me completely from any doubt as to my whereabouts that day a few months ago. I was just about to ask what had happened to Else when her daughter began to talk. It was at that moment I noticed every bit of the clothing she was wearing was black. I asked if Else had died and she repeated that I was not being questioned and that moreover, I was not under arrest. Their words were beginning to sound surreal.

"Not being questioned and not under arrest?" The only thing I did know was that, at this stage, I was not being accused of any wrongdoing. But what was the purpose of the whole interview? Sadly my wish to hear the reason was answered very soon and in a brutal way!

The detective began to talk very quietly. According to witnesses, Frau Stahl was seen on 29th December 1967 in the company of a young, smartly dressed man, leaving her house at approximately 10am. At about 7.30pm on the same evening, Frau Stahl returned to her house alone. She parked her car on the forecourt and slowly entered her house. She was heard to be crying.

One of the witnesses was a neighbour who had wanted to tell Else that her boyfriend was waiting for her inside the house. But since he had a key, the witness didn't know whether to tell her or not. As Else stepped into the hallway, the witnesses and neighbours from the next house heard a man's loud voice screaming: "Where are your young lovers?" (It was said in plural meaning many young lovers.) Then two shots were fired. Frau Stahl fell to the floor, her legs still in the doorway. There was silence. Frau Stahl was presumably dead. Then according to the witnesses, the voice shrieked again: "Where is your latest lover?" Within two minutes, there was another shot from the upper floor. And then it all went silent again. Frau Stahl's boyfriend had killed himself.

Finally the detective said that was all. The young lady asked if her mother had told me about her jealous boyfriend to which I replied that nothing was said about any 'jealous' boyfriend. I briefly told them how her mother had stopped for me just before the motorway towards Lucerne on her way home from shopping in Zurich and that I had been offered an overnight stay at her house.

I spoke about how we had had 'a constant giggle' and that she had become very fond of me but that we hadn't had any sexual contact. It was a lie to protect Else's dignity. I told her daughter how fondly her mother spoke of her and hadn't detected that Frau Stahl had any worries at all. I added that I did notice that she appeared to be very lonely and found in me a genuine and sincere young friend.

Her daughter confirmed to me that she was told the same thing just after six o'clock on the same evening when they met in Lucerne. Her daughter, who was also named Else, said that her mother had told her on that late afternoon how she was looking for me in Lucerne in the hope that she would find me still at the railway station.

The detective indicated that if I had I been in the house at the time, I would not be talking to them now. I was transfixed by the thought, not of what I was at that moment going through, but of the horror of poor Else's death. I couldn't talk any more. Suddenly a terrible grief took hold of me. My hands were trembling as the detective and Fraulein Stahl excused themselves, profoundly apologising for what they had put me through in the last hour. On the other hand, I felt deeply for young Fraulein Stahl. The encounter and the horrible tragedy shook me to the core.

I asked myself why these things kept happening to me. What on earth had I done to deserve this? When was it going to end?

Soon after that interview, I had a nervous breakdown or so I believe. I could not tell anybody what had happened, even the doctors. After two weeks I was able to work again and within two months I was back to a reasonable normality. I didn't take any medication nor did I have any counselling. I felt strong enough to pull through on my own.

I worked until the end of the season, went home for two months and then returned for the summer season to another tourist resort near St. Moritz where I stayed for the whole year.

In the spring of 1970 I had to go back to Yugoslavia to enlist for national service, with the constant ironic thought of how I had lost my fourth cat's life!

5
The Runaway Coach

It was June 1970 when I received my call up to do national service in Yugoslavia. I took a medical examination a month later and was declared fit to join the transport units in Croatia at the Adriatic harbour town of Rijeka. Almost immediately, as new conscripts we had to go through the ritual of having our hair shorn off completely and we were given an introductory speech by the major of our newly formed unit. The rules were outlined and we were warned of the punishment if we chose to ignore them.

The dining room at the barracks was capable of feeding up to three hundred recruits and older conscripts. What shocked me was the fact that the wooden tables were simply swiped with a damp cloth at the end of each session and the surface of the tables left wet. The bread was getting soaked and the metal plates still had bits of cabbage stuck to the bottom: clear evidence that they were not washed properly. The contrast with the hygiene standards I had been used to in the hotel in Switzerland was enormous. It made me heave. I began to toy with the idea of how to get out of the environment that I had been put in by the force of law.

I knew that I had to get away before the swearing-in ceremony because if I absconded after being sworn in, I would face a court martial and the punishment would be severe. I had four days left before the initiation. I planned to volunteer as a front gate guard because there was no immediate reason for any of the new recruits to try and abscond, hence the hard regime would only begin after the ceremony.

It worked! I was given a rifle which had, unbeknown to me, live ammunition. I was to stand guard in the company of a couple of older conscripts. I had one more reason to escape sooner rather than later: my high command headquarters was to receive my file from the authorities of my home town Maribor about two hundred miles away. I had been told by Rony (the neighbour of mine with whom I served the short prison sentence in Maribor during the aftermath of my botched attempt to escape to Austria) that I would have a hard time in national service. His words were: "Don't forget, Zdenko, you are now a marked man and in the eyes of the communist regime you are also classed as an enemy of the state."

I began to fantasise about how I would be singled out in front of the whole garrison and humiliated. I simply had no choice but to escape as soon as possible.

On the second day of my duty, I offered to my fellow guards to cross the main road and get some cigarettes from the shop there. They agreed. I left the rifle behind our little hut and crossed the road, but instead of going into the shop, I began to walk past. I increased my pace and ended up running down the road away from our post.

The alarm was raised as soon as the two conscripts saw me running. All hell broke loose and there were three or four military policemen chasing me, still thinking I was armed. I heard a few shots but didn't dare turn my head to see how far behind they were.

him on the day of his arrival at the office and couldn't wait to see him but the tour manager was waiting to give me bad news. Apparently my brother's friend, Joseph, did not want to join me. He added that he was slightly baffled as to why Joseph, coming from the same republic and town, refused to be housed in the same accommodation. I sensed that something was not right.

Eventually Joseph had no choice but to take the room next to mine and I even helped him with his luggage. However, his approach towards me was somehow hostile and I decided to leave him alone.

Our landlady, who occupied the rest of the beautiful neo-Austrian style mansion, would tease me on every occasion she saw me about how I managed to live such an active life and have so many girlfriends. But within days she became quite unfriendly and I came to the conclusion that Joseph must have said something bad about me.

It wasn't long before I was given another studio flat in the same area. There was no explanation as to why I had to leave the condo while Joseph remained. It was a busy time and I told myself that as soon as it was convenient, I would speak to my superior who was in Switzerland. Joseph was not good with languages and guests were complaining. I was informed that he wouldn't last long in his position and I told him that he should pull himself together. Unbeknown to me, Joseph realised that his days as a tour guide were numbered and he couldn't face defeat so wanted me to lose my position too. Many years later I found out that he regarded me as someone below him and believed he would lose face in our home town if he was sent packing. Luckily my superior and the rest of the management dismissed Joseph's stories about me and I ceased to have any meaningful contact with him for a good while.

Once a month we worked on a different tour. About a hundred and fifty miles away, near the town of Split, there was a tourist camp which housed and catered only for people coming from then communist Hungary, Eastern Germany, Poland, Czechoslovakia, Romania and other eastern European countries. Tito's regime had allowed those tourists to come to the Adriatic coast. Unfortunately, or fortunately for some, they had to stay in a specially-built area. They were allowed to swim in the sea in turns: once in the morning and once in the afternoon. They would go to do their little bit of shopping in groups of thirty and were under constant supervision by their own respective policemen.

I felt very sorry for them. They looked at us as if we were American because of our uniforms. I admit that those of us employed in the tourist industry had the best clothing and uniforms you could get in Yugoslavia. I would also buy a lot of clothes from English, German and Italian tourists that were on my tour, but I never gave the impression that I was desperate. The price was minimal, but nevertheless I paid for whatever I bought.

Before we entered the enclosure where the Eastern Europeans stayed, we were given the destination by their guards and instructions as to where we should make a stop.

My last tour with them had taken me to another coastal town, Rijeka - the very same place where I had been supposed to finish my national service.

The coach was full to the last seat despite the rainy weather. A lot of the passengers were wearing heavy raincoats that appeared to me to be a bit bulky. I was instructed to report anything unusual about their behaviour to one of their supervisors if necessary. I thought 'would I, my foot!' I naturally sensed that this group of eight bulkily-dressed tourists were on a clandestine mission but I wasn't allowed to chat to them because of their guards' fear that they might hear something which would incite them to try and abscond to the Italian territory nearby.

Our last stop was at the small harbour town just north of Koper, about ten miles from the Italian border. All of the eight tourists dressed in raincoats were sitting at the end of the restaurant terrace facing the sea which was just a stone's throw away.

All at once there was a commotion in the restaurant area. The Hungarian guards swiftly moved in that direction while the group of eight tourists wearing those heavy raincoats suddenly jumped over the low terrace railings and made their way towards the Italian border! My tour driver Momo looked at me and wanted to go and inform the guards (who had been busy with the small group of our tour at the other end of the restaurant) but I calmly told him that they had already been apprehended by other guards. Of course it was a lie.

Momo was worried about his duty to keep an eye on all the

passengers. I assured him that I would not go after them because in their desperation to flee the country they might do all sorts of things such as stabbing or shooting.

"Besides, we are not policemen" I told him.

The commotion at the other end had stopped and the two guards came to our table and enquired about the eight passengers that had been sitting next to us. Momo exclaimed that they should know better. I said that I had seen the group leaving about five minutes earlier and that I had spotted somebody running after them.

By now I was hoping and praying that they were on their way towards the Italian border. What I hadn't told Momo and the guards was the fact I knew from the very start of our journey that the eight passengers had deflated car tyre inner tubes hidden underneath their raincoats. Even today I still hope that they made it to Italy across the narrow bay which divided the two countries.

The two guards made an official complaint to our superiors and we were asked to write a full report. Nothing came of it, although Momo and I never had to take any more tourists from that camp site ever again. Deep inside I was pleased with what I had done since the whole episode had reminded me of my attempt to illegally cross the border a few years back.

The management was not very pleased about what had happened and was worried that I might be talking to the Brits and Germans about political issues. For about a month I noticed that every driver recorded my speech on the coach. I had to be careful. I also felt sudden changes amongst other tour guides in the way they spoke to me. I had the feeling that the management had made some enquiries about me. I was expecting that at any moment the truth would come out about my past in Maribor. A few days passed and I went again to see Werner, the guide who had asked me to join the company.

Werner was very open and told me that a lot of other tour guides were very jealous of me, including Joseph, and that Joseph was spreading all sorts of terrible things about me. Apparently I was second on the list for the highest tips. I wanted to go and see Joseph straight away and punch him on the nose.

Werner also warned me that it had not been a good idea when I had punched one of the drivers in the stomach after he had stolen all the tips which we were supposed to share. Despite all the other drivers supporting me, I realised that my temper had got the better of me and consequences would surely follow.

I asked Werner what the outlook was for me at the company. He said that I should slow down a bit with my night life and not to have so many parties at my accommodation. I blamed Joseph who had been bad news for me right from the day he refused to share the apartment. I swore to myself that I would take revenge and decided not to cause any more trouble while still in Dubrovnik, remembering that 'revenge is a dish best served cold'.

Werner came out with an idea to quieten everything down. He gave me a tour to Turkey - to Istanbul to be precise. There would be around one hundred and thirty American tourists onboard a charter plane. All I had to do was make sure that they were in a good mood throughout the tour. The rest would be left to the local guide. Of course I had to keep them together and count them continuously.

There was one more thing. I had to do some shopping for the management and the list was as long as my arm. It turned out to be the biggest smuggling job I ever did!

The following day Werner handed me over all the paperwork: passengers' passports, flight tickets, in short whatever was needed for the trip. The Americans were busy with their shopping and so was I. After three days we had to return to Dubrovnik.

I had a look at my bags and the shopping that had been listed and I had no idea how I would be able to get through the Yugoslav customs at Dubrovnik airport. I began to put on four layers of shirts, then three pairs of jeans and four watches on each arm. I stuffed all the other items where I could. I looked at least three sizes bigger than I was before the tour. It was hilarious. The Americans were falling over from laughing.

On our arrival at the airport I asked the air steward to go before me towards the exit and the customs entrance. I waited on the plane with the pilots since they had a lot of shopping on them as well. I was the last to go through customs. When they saw me, they burst out laughing too. One of the customs officials called me into his office and told me that it had all been pre-arranged and that I should take the clothes off. I was sweating profusely. Some of the shopping was for several of the customs officers themselves. 'Well', I thought to myself, 'this is how the country is run'.

That was the last good laugh I had for a long time. A few weeks later, I was to cry my eyes out! It was Monday, 11th July 1971. The night before, it had been raining but it had cleared during the early hours of the morning. I was strolling along the path towards our coach garage about five minutes away from where I lived. The orange trees were in full bloom and the air was scented by them. I finished my sandwich and boarded the coach which was marked 'Montenegro Tour'. The driver was nowhere to be seen. I waited and waited. After about ten minutes I decided to go and look for the driver.

As tour guides, we would all have the plans and vouchers delivered to our doorsteps the evening before. The dispatcher told me that I was late and that the driver and guide had left about an hour earlier. I told the dispatcher that I had never ever been late and showed him my paperwork.

He began to scratch his forehead and grabbed the handle of his radio transmitter. He tried to call the driver and guide but their radio was switched off. The dispatcher, whose name was Meho, started to rant about how disorganised his department was. Meho apologised for his outburst and after he had another look at my vouchers, suggested that I take a company driver with his saloon car and try to catch up "with those two idiots". To make matters worse the tour guide in question spoke only Italian and the group for that excursion consisted of Germans and Brits. There would be a serious complaint afterwards and rightfully the money would have to be returned. It was not just a matter of refunding the money.

The Runaway Coach

The representatives could boycott the company as well.

I jumped into the car and we sped off towards some of the hotels to see if they were still picking up their passengers. The porters told us that they had left about an hour earlier. We joined the highway and broke all the speed limits on that stretch of road. The surface was very slippery because the rainfall on the previous night had released grease forming a fatty layer floating above the wet road surface. Twice we nearly ended up in the ditches running alongside the road. There was no sign of the coach.

We flagged down another coach driver to find out if they had seen the 'runaway' coach. We had been on the road well over an hour when my supervisor contacted me to find out whether I was on the right coach. "Negative," I replied.

"Please try to find those two idiots" were his words. My driver knew all the short-cuts of the route which the coach driver could have taken. But the coach had simply vanished.

I told my driver that I was not prepared to take over the tour if and when we found them fearing that I would have to take all the flak from the presumably disappointed passengers.

We finally caught a glimpse of the coach way up on the mountain. The driver calculated the distance and the height where they were, the condition of the road and the time it would take him to reach the speeding coach. He agreed with me that it would be counter-productive to make a changeover. We resigned ourselves to that fact and turned around and headed back towards Dubrovnik.

I got on the radio and told my supervisor of my decision and he agreed. We had been driving for about twenty minutes or so when the message came through the radio communication that we were to turn round immediately and rush back towards the area where we last saw the coach.

As we drove closer there were police cordoning off the road. We were on the second bend and below the point where we had last seen the coach. I told the driver that the coach had probably broken down and the police were only securing the area.

We came to a halt at a newly erected road block. My driver spoke to one of the policemen and explained that we were from the same travel agency and that we were going to drive to the spot where we could turn around. After about a hundred yards we saw a coach of the same colour and logo as our missing coach turned upside down beneath the road we were on. The coachwork looked battered and one of the wheels was still slowly spinning.

Then came the horrific screams from all directions. My driver and I jumped over the makeshift barrier and began to run towards the crashed coach. I looked frantically for anyone still moving. I probably stepped on some body parts while running from one casualty to another. I was screaming at the top of my voice: "Where are the ambulances?!!"

The scene was shocking. There were bodies strewn all over the place. Severed limbs were hanging from small bushes. The smell was indescribable. There were shoes lying scattered around us. After a while, ambulances appeared from all directions. My driver and I stopped and paused again for a moment. I started to run again towards the rear of the coach where there were some more people crying and asking for help. A group of soldiers appeared in front of me and shouted for me to go away. I was persistent and tried to enter the coach through the broken side window to fetch some cold drinks that were normally kept in a small fridge but I was pulled back out by two soldiers. They began to carry me towards a police car.

One of the policemen wanted to arrest me for hindering the rescue operation. I remember barking at him that he should instead jump over the ramp and help the injured and dying instead of talking to me about arrest! He noticed my travel agency badge and handed me over to the ambulance team, maybe realising how stupid he looked! At that point I was enraged and didn't care about being arrested and forcibly taken away.

We were both escorted to our car. The driver and I broke down in tears. We sat on the road kerb and talked in whispers about the tragedy that had just happened, certain that a lot of people had died that morning. Even to this day, the scene comes back into my mind. Up until then, I had only seen similar carnage when watching a war film.

After we had composed ourselves, my driver blurted out some words as if to say that I had had a lucky escape. My reply was: "Yes that is the story of my life."

It transpired that the tour guide on the coach had changed the rota papers the night before. His name was Jappa and he had wanted to take over the excursion only because that particular tour yielded the most tips at the end. He stupidly thought that he could do as well as me, forgetting that, in order to receive gratuities, a tour guide has to do lots of work such as acting as a waiter and serving food to the tables when needed. Above all, he would have to have known the required language reasonably well.

I found out on the same day that there were nineteen people dead. Mostly, they had been thrown through the windows as the coach tumbled down the hill. The driver was badly injured and never drove again, Jappa the guide, who was sitting in the front seat, was wedged between the two arm rests so wasn't thrown through the windscreen at the time of impact: his obese body was found still stuck in his seat. Had I, with my nine stone weight, sat on that designated front seat, I would have been thrown straight through the windshield and almost certainly been squashed under the tumbling coach. Sadly, Jappa was badly injured and ended up in a wheelchair. All those years ago there were no laws in my country regarding compulsory seat belts.

An official enquiry was set up and their findings were very damning:

1. The coach had two badly worn rear tyres.
2. The speed was inappropriate for the prevailing road and traffic conditions.
3. Seat belts were not fitted in the coach.
4. Possible driver fatigue.

4
Desert Ambush

In the aftermath of the tragedy of the crash, the hardest and saddest thing was to meet the relatives of the victims and to accompany some of them to the spot of the accident. I wasn't asked by my travel agency to do that, but a few of the relatives had somehow found out where I lived and pleaded with me to take them there. I suppose it was crucial for them to have closure. Upon our return, they tried to pay for the loss of my earnings for that day. How could I have accepted their payment?

Later on I found out that I would have been in big trouble if the authorities had discovered I had taken those relatives to the place of the accident because a thorough investigation was still ongoing and by law, I would have been in contempt of court. I was still young and at the time didn't think about the possible consequences but if I faced a similar situation I would probably do the same thing again.

I was sure from that fateful day onwards that there was nothing I could do to change the course of my life. I didn't dwell on it. Destiny. Destiny.

I stayed on for the next few months. It was September 1973 when I decided to go to South Africa after the summer season in Dubrovnik. I had met a couple of South Africans on one of my tours. They told me that I could easily find a similar post as a tour guide in Cape Town. They offered to help me out until I found my own way financially but I had saved quite a bit of money and so did not need that kind of help.

I charted my course whereby the route would take me from

Dubrovnik to Sicily, from there through Libya, Egypt and Sudan and then by sea to South Africa. When I mentioned my plans to a few of my workmates, they thought that my idea was ludicrous and fraught with danger but I had already made up my mind to carry it out. There were not many choices for me. I had no home to go to. What money I had sent home while working in Switzerland had long gone as I mentioned before. The prospect of staying with my aunty did not appeal to me either.

Although my Swiss work permit could be renewed, I had resolved to try my luck in South Africa. Why, I will never know. I could have gone to the States. At that time the Westinghouse Corporation was building a nuclear reactor on the border between today's Republic of Slovenia and Croatia. Every so often the corporate employees would spend a few days in Dubrovnik as a perk of the job. On one occasion I was touring with a small group of four Westinghouse employees. I gave them very good service as I always did. They were not spying on the country since they knew more of our system (perhaps much more) than I did. I was more curious than they were and asked them a lot of questions.

When we had lunch together in Ljubljana, I asked them why they were building the reactor in Slovenia and not somewhere in Serbia that had the River Danube with much more reactor cooling water than here. I was told that Yugoslavia would inevitably break up after Marshall Tito's death and that the nuclear facility would be best protected in Slovenia because of the proximity of Italy which was in NATO. I connected the dots and concluded that this was the reason Tito was not willing to pass on the presidency to any of his cabinet members before his death.

I found the nuclear engineers to be overly nice so I somehow misunderstood their offer for me to come to the USA and join their corporation as a sexual proposition. Due to my cultural differences I assumed at least two of them were gay. I was ignorant at the time of liberal Western culture and misunderstood their intentions. So no USA.

At the same time I was also offered a post as a travel rep for Swedish Airlines in Dubrovnik over the summer season and in Austria for the winter. Instead I chose the option to go and live in South Africa!

It was 29th September when I boarded a ferry to Naples and from there to the port of Trapani on the southern coast of Sicily. From there, another ferry took me to the port of Tunis.

Upon my arrival in Tunisia things did not go the way I planned. I was forced to change all but a few hundred US dollars into their currency. The rest I had to hide in my socks. Somehow customs did not search me. Looking back, I wish they had done just that. In the process I would have lost all my money and faced probable expulsion. But at least from there I would have been forced to go back to Switzerland.

When I reached the capital Tunis, there were the first signs of possible delays. It was their bank holiday which lasted for four days. The Libyan embassy was closed for the next ten. All the time I was thinking of how much money I would spend and how I could change their currency back to US dollars.

I managed to find a person who was willing to give me a reasonable exchange rate. After a calculation I realised that of seventeen hundred US dollars which were exchanged upon my arrival, the sum had dwindled to a mere twelve hundred. What a waste after being in the country for only a few days! It was too late to try and continue my journey by air because a plane ticket would have cost me about eight hundred dollars. After the conversion I would still have had to exchange all my money into Tunisian dinars. Because I had chosen not to comply with the country's financial laws, to be safe, I decided to continue the rest of the journey by road.

While waiting for the Libyan embassy to open, I made some enquiries about the railway connections between the two countries. Unfortunately there were no railway connections! After all my years of organising these things for others, this was not the best example of a tour guide and a coordinator!

In general, the Tunisian people were extremely nice to me. I was invited into many houses to discuss topics such as global politics. Their president at the time was Bourgiba and his more intellectually curious citizens were interested to hear what was going on in the rest of the world. Again I must stress that they were very hospitable. With the help of a professor who I met at the coffee bar in Tunis, I found a job at one of the hotels in Djerba, a tourist resort on the coast, just to get used to the climate. It also gave me more time to change my plans and abandon the perilous journey altogether.

The professor, whose name was Ali, took me to the hotel and the manager employed me straight away, mainly because they had a lot of tourists from Yugoslavia staying at the hotel. Unfortunately for me, after a week I had to leave because of their immigration laws.

I went back to the Libyan embassy in Tunis. My visa was valid for only twenty days. I had to find the cheapest means of transport that would take me through Tunisian territory into Libya itself, then through the whole of Libya towards Egypt and along the coastline towards Sudan. Just the thought that I didn't even check whether there was a railway link between Tunisia and Libya still to this day makes me angry! I haggled a bit about the price to get me from Sousse to Tripoli. In those days there were not many coaches going to Tripoli. People had to travel mainly by small converted Peugeot pick-ups. They were licensed to carry up to ten people and had an open top. The trip from Sousse to Cairo would have cost me a hundred and eighty US dollars. I was desperate to leave Tunisia because all my remaining money was dwindling very fast but I didn't want to pay for the whole trip in one go in case there were problems with the various relief drivers. I was told that the whole journey would take about three days.

I had to make another quick calculation to see if there was enough money for the whole journey to South Africa by road. I had seven hundred US dollars in cash and a few hundred German marks, a gold watch and a twenty-two carat gold chain which I had bought in Switzerland. My only worry was the foreign currency which was supposed to have been exchanged in Tunisia a few weeks earlier. I would have had the same problem had I decided to simply go back to Tunis

was what were their intentions? Had they wanted to, they could have robbed me on the very first night. If Marcel and Salvatore should physically attack and rob me, the odds were in their favour. I was on my own, I didn't know anybody in the country and was thousands of kilometres away from my home. I had no means to defend myself other than some knowledge of martial arts which I had acquired in my hometown years before as a Scout. It was the only weapon I had. I hadn't learned this skill for the purpose of attacking anybody but solely to use as a last resort when in danger. Equally, I was quite good at running. How I wished to be near any of the local rivers but of course there were none.

I also noticed that Salvatore wore a jacket with bulging pockets. Was he armed and what for? I had come to the conclusion that I should at least, in any event, try and put up a fight and somehow wrench any possible weapon out of Salvatore's hands. But what about Marcel and what would he do? All these questions were racing through my mind.

Throughout the journey from our last stopover in the town of Medinine late in the afternoon, I tried to move my feet under the wooden benches that we were sitting on. But the sacks that I mentioned earlier were there which Asim had told me were filled with flour or wheat. I found it very irritating because I couldn't move my legs freely. The sacks had something in black ink written on them. It said in English that it was aid from the International Red Cross. There were six of them. My lower legs were itching because they were rubbing against the rough fabric of the sacks. The heat was immense and I was sweating profoundly. There was sand everywhere: in my eyes, ears, hair and shoes. The other passengers were mostly dressed in their traditional black robes and they seemed to bear the heat without any problems. They conversed in their language but every so often I could hear some of their words were in French. I knew from my school history lessons that Tunisia had been under French rule some ten years before. Salvatore wanted to ask one of the passengers about something but the driver stepped in and told him in Italian that he should try not to talk at all. I was beginning to become aware of the relationship between them and wondered if I would I be their prey.

It was obvious that Marcel did not know the present driver and it looked as if Salvatore hadn't known Marcel for very long, therefore, logically, they must have had some kind of instructions from another person. Most definitely they had a plan which had been worked out by somebody else. Coming from a communist country myself, I began to think that maybe they were on a mission of a different kind. The Libyan leader Gaddafi had overthrown the previous regime in a military coup. What if those three were part of a group to possibly overthrow the Colonel? I began to plan how to switch to another car which would follow in a few hours time.

We still had at least sixty kilometres to travel before we reached the Libyan border. I felt drained of energy and had to nod off every so often, only to wake up again within moments. Then I suddenly thought that the solution could be very simple. At the next stop I would grab my little travel bag and jump out of the truck. Surely, I thought, these three people wouldn't dare do me any harm in front of all the people who might be waiting at the next stop to board the truck.

The sky had become darker and dusk would follow soon. We had reached the last small town where I hoped to try and jump out. Suddenly the driver changed his mind and accelerated through the town without picking anybody up. There were eight of us left on board plus the driver. Those other five passengers didn't say a word as the driver drove on with considerable speed. They just sat there.

The driver took the next turning onto the road which also led towards the border except that this road was running parallel to the A1 road a few hundred yards away. I was expecting that at any moment the truck would stop and probably be joined by more people coming from somewhere nearby, or possibly another truck. The whole detour had made me go numb. The instinct for survival had probably kicked in.

The five passengers suddenly began to draw guns from underneath their robes and with the speed of lightning beat Marcel and Salvatore over their heads with the guns. They brought Marcel and Salvatore down to the floor of the truck. The whole thing happened within the blink of an eye. I was certain that it was my turn next.

They blindfolded the driver, Marcel and Salvatore. One of the five passengers who had turned into a 'car-jacker' wanted to kill all three of them on the spot, but another of the group stopped him. Instead, the three were thrown out of the truck. The man who had prevented the other guy from shooting them began to talk to me in French. I tried hard to concentrate on what he said. These men were from Algiers and were trying to reach Libyan soil that night. I should not fear them. As far as they were concerned, I was just an innocent traveller. They would take me along to Tripoli and after that I would be on my own.

To this day I can't describe how I felt. There was only one more thing. Why were they still wearing scarves over their faces? I dared not ask them. My head was spinning with all the things that had happened in such a short space of time.

By then my back was hurting because of the rough road we were on. We returned onto the main road again. They put their guns away and took some food out of their baskets. They offered me some and I hadn't the slightest idea what it was but in any case it tasted delicious and it looked clean: some kind of kebab-like food which had been nicely wrapped in white paper. I drew the conclusion that they must have come from a well-to-do background.

The way they spoke was in total contrast to what they had done to the driver, Marcel and Salvatore a mere half an hour ago! Although it was dark, for the first time in three days, I began to take note of the vegetation and the shape of palm trees along the road. About every ten minutes there were cars passing us in the opposite direction. Some of them were hooting or giving us a signal with their headlights flashing. Their leader asked me how I had ended up in Tunisia in the first place. I told him in a few words the reason. He appeared to be amused. Why had I left Europe while most people from the African continent eagerly wanted to go just there? I replied that my real destination was South Africa. He nodded. I asked him how far we were from the border and he said that it would take at least two more hours. I presumed that he had a reason not to tell me his name although I told him what my name was.

The minutes seemed like hours. The huge palm trees were visible in the bright moonlight and the sand dunes stretched away on both sides of the road. Every so often I noticed in the distance the silhouettes of the mosque spires interrupting the straight line of the barely-visible horizon. The cold air was blowing on my face. It felt like the late autumn temperatures back in Europe. My thoughts were concentrated on how crossing the border ahead of us would end. The car-jackers were still wearing their scarves around their faces and I wondered how they could possibly pass through the border control veiled like that. I couldn't figure out whether Marcel and Salvatore had belonged to a different splinter group and the bunch of car-jackers had been tipped off to ambush them. One thing appeared to be certain: both groups were involved in something illegal and I was right in the middle of it all and couldn't change anything.

I began to resent these people that were holding me prisoner. I asked the leader to let me go and that I would not tell anybody what had happened. The leader didn't want to hear anything about letting me go. I asked him why and he replied that I would be useful to them in the future. I immediately realised that they had no intention of letting me go after we had crossed the border. At least I now knew what their plan was regarding me. I switched into self-defence mode just as I had done in my home town when standing up to the bigger boys who were trying to bully me. I knew how the group's Kalashnikovs worked and that they carried Browning and Walter hand guns. Most commonly these were the 7.65mm calibre.

Although I had fired all manner of firearms including hand guns during my compulsory pre-army training back home, I had never owned and carried any type of armoury around with me. When I was younger, the boys who I went swimming with in the river next to my home had found a lot of well-preserved guns and often shot them into the air until they ran out of ammunition. They would throw the empty guns into the river and wait for another one to be found. Never did any of my friends threaten the general public with them. The only true delinquent amongst them was Milo with whom I had crossed the Austrian border years before. Yes, we would sometimes go so far as to pinch some of the tomatoes from the fields on our way to the river; or to help ourselves to a neighbour's peaches but who hasn't done that occasionally in their youth?

There I was, trying to avoid using any force involving a gun, but I was ready if necessary to shoot someone. I never even carried a knife with me but now I had to do something to stay alive! I kept whispering to myself to stay calm but my whole body was trembling with fear, not a fear of dying but a fear of dying slowly.

I had to work fast. The border crossing was coming closer and closer. The leader asked me to hand over my passport to him. I did so reluctantly and the leader must have sensed that I might be awkward. I was certain that he would simply get rid of me as soon as we entered Libya. I was determined not to die in some far flung country for nothing. At least I could make it very difficult for them.

Now, all sorts of things began to appear in front of my eyes. I can still vividly remember to this day how it seemed as though film clips depicting my life were being played out in chronological order. My mother's face came up after each episode. All of a sudden the whole situation ceased to bother me. The fear had gone and I began to work out whether I could grab one of the Kalashnikovs that was lying at the feet of a car-jacker. We came to a halt at the road block manned by young Tunisians - possibly conscripts just as in Yugoslavia - and we were asked to produce our travel documents. One of the young soldiers demanded that the leader give my passport to me and that I should present myself with my passport in future. It was this young soldier's remarks that later saved me.

I nearly blurted out that I had been kidnapped and was being forced to stay on the truck against my will but one of the car-jackers pressed a Kalashnikov barrel against my ribs from behind and out of sight of the young soldier. The border crossing wasn't lit well enough for the solder to see the suspicious behaviour of the leader or the machine gun being pressed into my back. I was hoping that once we were near the small metallic hut ahead of us, there would be a chance for me to grab the leader and, with whatever strength I still had, to push us both over the truck's side. I didn't care if it was going to break my neck. I just wanted to end the situation one way or another.

The young conscript came back with our passports and gave me a look, asking in French if I was all right. I only nodded. I still remember that the soldier who was dealing with our truck spent a long time talking to someone. I hoped that somebody from the border control would come over to us. Instead he told the driver to move forward towards the police kiosk some ten yards in front of us. The car-jacker who still had his machine gun pressed into my ribs spoke to the police officer sitting in the small kiosk under a giant tent and I had a funny feeling that they knew each other. He made a hand gesture to proceed to the customs kiosk a few yards ahead. There was nobody in the booth. It seemed to me that all the personnel had disappeared from their posts. I guessed that they had been instructed by their superior to disappear for a while so that our truck could drive through unhindered. I turned my head to see where some sudden calls came from. There was a commotion back at the Tunisian check point and I could see the Tunisian border guards gesturing with their hands up in the air and shouting in our direction but our driver continued slowly towards the Libyan border. At that moment we were in no man's land. It stretched for about four hundred yards, sandwiched between Tunisian and Libyan check points. The car-jackers obviously knew the area and probably some of the personnel at the Libyan border.

We came to a sudden halt and the driver swung himself onto the back where we were sitting on the benches on both sides. He pulled out one of the sacks that was underneath my legs. With a knife in his left hand, whose polished blade was illuminated by the moonlight, he cut the top of the sack open and what looked like flour began to pour onto the floor of the truck. He then scooped some of the white substance with the tip of his knife and rubbed it between his fingers. He was the last passenger remaining from Sousse. It then became obvious that he had been the real leader of the group the whole time. The white stuff that appeared to be nothing more than flour turned out to be either cocaine or an explosive of some sort! I had never seen what cocaine looked like, neither had I seen up until then what an explosive in loose form looked like either. In either case, I had a feeling that I was sitting on a keg of gunpowder.

While watching the driver as he was busy with the illicit cargo, I heard Marcel's voice shout in French: "C'est fini c'est fini" meaning the end! They had appeared out of the middle of nowhere! All the car-jackers including the driver were taken by surprise. Salvatore had his machine gun aimed at our driver and when the driver tried to draw his gun he was mown down by Salvatore's weapon in an instant. I knew that peppering bullets would spray the steel inside of the truck and that at any moment I could be hit by a straying or ricocheted bullet. I crawled towards the cabin end of the truck and pressed my body to the metal flooring. The cackling of the machine guns and pistols was going on and on. Then I felt a pain in my left thigh.

At first, I thought I had imagined it: all the adrenalin

pumping through my veins must have caused a false sensation. But the pain became more intense with every second passing and I knew that I had actually been wounded. The shooting stopped and I peeped through a small hole made by one of the machine gun bullets on the side panel to see who was in control of the situation.

Marcel was lying, presumably dead, a few yards away. Our driver and his four accomplices were slumped on the floor a few inches apart in front of me. Their blood was forming a small pool which was getting bigger and edging towards the spot where I had been lying. I had a feeling that their blood and strong smelling urine was beginning to soak into my long leather coat. I could clearly hear the engine running and the revs increasing as the truck jerked forward. I couldn't see who was driving it.

The truck began to move and was veering to the left. I concluded that it must be driving on its own because of the automatic transmission, and that the handbrake had somehow released itself. We were heading in the direction of the Libyan border check point.

I was frantic and didn't know what to do. Should I jump out of the truck and run back towards the Tunisian border? I could see that some of the border patrol on the Tunisian side were beginning to approach the moving truck. Would they think that I had something to do with the shooting? I felt that at least the young Tunisian soldier from the border control could help me explain to his superiors that he had had a suspicion I was an unwilling participant in what had just happened.

I didn't want to end up on Libyan territory for the simple reason that I would be looked upon as a trespasser and end up in prison almost immediately. And then I would probably be made answerable for all the dead people around me.

I decided to swing myself into the truck cabin and managed to steer the truck around towards the bushes about a hundred yards from the Tunisian check point. The bushes were quite thick and stopped the truck from going any further.

I abandoned it and began to make my way, limping into the darkness of the undergrowth, expecting at any moment to be caught by the Tunisian border patrol. Nothing happened. It all went eerily quiet. The whole episode had probably lasted about eight to ten minutes while it felt like an eternity. My mind went blank. I was aware that my motions had became more robotic and my brain was telling me to move as far away as possible, and fast! I had realised that my holdall was left behind.

What was I supposed to do next? I could hear various loud voices. Some sounded like yelled commands coming from the Tunisian check point. The pain had become excruciating and I felt blood running down my left leg. I changed my plan and instead of giving myself up decided I would try to circumnavigate the check point on the Tunisian side. After that I would try to reach Tunis by hitch-hiking. I wanted to be away from the border crossing since presumably they were all involved in the whole affair.

I couldn't hear any voices behind me and concluded that the search had concentrated towards the Libyan side of the border. I must have stepped countless times on snakes and scorpions but didn't get bitten.

I progressed very slowly because of my injury. I was dehydrated, hungry and above all mentally exhausted. How I had found the strength to run for about five miles along the main road towards the nearest town, I will never know.

Dawn was approaching and I decided to try my luck and stop a car going in the direction of Tunis. Some four or five cars passed without stopping. Then the next car came to a screeching halt. The driver was in uniform and asked me whether I was all right in French. I didn't say anything hoping that he would see that I obviously wasn't. He opened the passenger door and we drove off.

He asked me where I was heading and as I mentioned Sousse he enquired whether I was a lost tourist because by then, Sousse was already a known tourist resort. He spoke to me in a sort of fatherly way. He said that very often tourists from Djerba and Sousse would go to Libya for a day or so and he asked whether I had left my friends back in Libya. I told him that I was travelling alone and had missed my coach going back to my resort. He slowed down as we approached a lay-by, stopped the car and had a close look at me. I could see that he looked worried. He said that he knew what had happened a few hours earlier at the border crossing. He told me that he knew what must have happened to me. He asked me if I remembered a soldier at the check point who had advised me to keep my passport on me all the time. I confirmed this and he explained that the conscript had told him, as his officer, to keep an eye on me because he sensed that things were not okay. Unfortunately, the car-jackers had driven through while the border police officer was phoning him about me. His phone had fallen on the floor and the car-jackers had used that moment to drive past him.

He gave me a bottle of water which I gulped down in a few seconds so he gave me another. Then he offered me some home-cooked baked potatoes filled with tuna. After a few moments he spotted that my left trouser leg was covered with dried blood. He had a first aid kit in his car and tried to wrap a bandage around my left thigh. I could feel the bullet but also that the main artery was not ruptured. However, any movements could have done just that so I begged him to take me to the nearest hospital. Because I kept my leather coat on throughout this time, only my hands and face appeared scratched and bruised.

The officer, whose name was Habib, had some relatives living abroad and understood what it meant to be in a foreign country. He assured me that he was not a member of any gang. But at the same time he advised me that if he did take me to hospital the truth of how I got that bullet in my thigh would come out and I would spend many months, probably years, on remand. I didn't know what to believe. Was he just doing this to gain some time to somehow cover up the whole thing? Was Habib really his name? I began to bleed again and had no choice but to believe him.

He said that we had to drive somewhere off the main road and that I should try to remove the bullet myself. He had some painkillers and antiseptic in his kit. I really had no other choice but to go along with his plan. Even the thought that he might be lying to me and finish me off didn't bother me. I was at the end of my tether.

When I realised that he genuinely felt sorry for me and did not draw his gun, I believed and trusted him. I began to cut off the trouser leg and with his pocket knife started to prise the lodged bullet out of the wound. I could clearly see that the wound had already gone septic. In normal circumstances I would probably have screamed in pain but I did not.

I put a piece of the fabric that came from the torn trouser leg in my mouth and bit on it very hard. I never knew previously that someone could do what I did without fainting. I finally got the bullet out and showed it to Habib. I had tears in my eyes which were not due to my emotional state but the pain.

He looked at my wound again and said that we should immediately go to his home where he would give me fresh clothes and take me straight to the hospital. Habib then changed his mind as he didn't want anybody to see the state I was in and took me somewhere near his home where I had to wait for him in his car.

He brought me a fresh shirt, a pair of trousers, a pair of flip flops, a pair of underpants and a few wet towels. He drove me back to the main road and we stopped at another lay-by where I changed into the fresh clothes. For the first time I looked at myself in the rear view mirror. I was in a really bad state. No wonder Habib had taken pity on me. Being in great pain, I rubbed my hands and face with the wet towels which smelt of disinfectant. Habib suggested that we drive to one of the hospitals in Tunis. He made it very clear that I must under no circumstances reveal how I got my wound and scratches. I had to maintain that I fell off the train at La Marsa and that I had lost all my papers and money. He would come to visit me in the hospital the following day.

I gave him my passport, all the papers I had and about four hundred US dollars. He said he would see to it that the remaining local currency was changed into Swiss francs. He assured me that everything would be fine as long as I did things the way he suggested. He would destroy all the papers and the passport.

He took me to the biggest hospital in Tunis. The doctors were not sure whether they could save my leg. I was operated on within half an hour. When I woke up from the general anaesthetic, Habib was standing next to my bed. Beside him was a woman who I presumed to be his wife. I couldn't talk and they left after a while. I could see that the woman had tears in her eyes but I could not say a word although I wanted to.

The next day I had a visit from the Yugoslav embassy in Tunis. They wanted to know what had happened. I told them exactly what Habib had instructed me to say. They left me some fruit and said that they would have to look into the matter and pay me a visit before my discharge from hospital.

Habib and his wife Saifa came to visit me every day. After a fortnight I was visited by a Yugoslav consul and told that I would have to come on the day of my discharge to the embassy to collect a duplicate passport. They would try to arrange a plane ticket to Belgrade.

Habib took me to the embassy and said that he would wait for me. The embassy staff had quite a different idea. They suspected that I had something to do with the border shooting since they had found a Yugoslav passport on one of the dead men. They also told me that there were shootings quite often on that border.

I denied it completely. I was certain that they would have beaten me had it not been for Habib. He rang the bell a few times and the embassy staff thought that Habib was a policeman and someone in authority so they allowed me to leave the room and talk to him.

Of course they had listening devices in that room and Habib put his forefinger to his lips to indicate that we should avoid talking about anything in connection with the shootings. When I returned, the interrogating officer at the embassy changed his tactics. He wanted to know how I came to know Habib. He was hoping that I was some kind of young spy or something similar. I told him that I had met Habib in Dubrovnik on one of my tours as a tour guide. After a while he became more pleasant and said that if all of that was true I should sign a statement and after an exchange of a few telexes to Maribor, Belgrade and Dubrovnik I would be issued with a new passport and a single plane ticket to Belgrade. I was not allowed to leave before they got positive answers.

Habib was (I presumed) still waiting and within the following two hours, the embassy received all the answers, namely that I had a military police record for my conduct when I absconded and I had avoided national service but that there were no outstanding warrants for my arrest. So, according to their records and in the eyes of the communist embassy staff, I was not a desirable citizen but nevertheless, I was not involved in any crime.

I stayed at the embassy compound for another day. Maybe they just wanted to make sure that I wasn't wanted by the Tunisian authorities. I was told that the passport given to them by the Tunisian authorities was false and that I didn't match the description or look anything like the photo in that false passport. My instinct told me that the passport was Marcel's doing.

Habib and Saifa, along with the Yugoslav deputy consul, saw me off at Tunis airport. Habib spoke to me in French and I could see that the deputy consul spoke no French so could not understand our short conversation. Habib gave me his address and told me that I should get an Austrian address where he would send me my money. They both wanted to come to Dubrovnik the following summer.

While on the plane to Yugoslavia, I kept telling myself that I must have been a reincarnated cat from my previous life and therefore I must have nine lives. Quite a few were already spent! Would I ever reach the ninth life and when?

When I arrived at Belgrade airport there were two policemen waiting for me. They took me to a police station and gave me a thorough search. They were looking for my original passport and whether I had any money on me. I wasn't surprised at all.

They suspected that Habib had given me a false passport and money. They questioned me about my links with Habib and his wife Saifa. I kept telling them that the married couple were touring our country and I had happened to be one of their tour guides in Dubrovnik a year earlier. I said they helped me after I fell off the train.

One of the interrogators showed me a cutting of the Tunisian national paper where it said in French and Arabic that seven people had been shot, all of whom were well-known criminals. One of them was a Yugoslav national. He came from Bosnia, being one of the republics of what was then Yugoslavia. The policeman who led my interrogation wanted to know if I had any knowledge of the incident since I allegedly fell off the train on the very same day. I denied having any knowledge of a shooting during my short stay in Tunisia.

Apparently the Tunisian police had come to the hospital but didn't bother to talk to me since the person who had the Yugoslav passport was approximately one foot taller with a chubby build and jet black hair so simply didn't bear any resemblance to me. I did not think for one minute that Habib had used my passport in connection with the terrible crime I had witnessed a month earlier.

The Belgrade police had to let me go because there was no link between me and the car-jackers whose lives had ended in the style in which they lived. Habib sent me my money through an Austrian address in small amounts in case the envelope went missing. In the last letter with the money, Habib also enclosed my passport and advised me to take it to the Yugoslav authorities to have my name taken off their files. How could he have known so many of our laws?

I had Habib's phone number and I rang him about four months later. He wanted to know if I had received all of the money and the passport. I asked him how his wife was and stated that I would one day like to visit them. I thanked him for all he had done for me. He also mentioned that they had had some more similar incidents since I had met him and that he was worried where all the drugs would end up.

After a long conversation I wanted to know why he had gone through so much trouble to help me, putting them both at risk. He paused for a while and said that as a young man, he had once been accused of a robbery in Paris and a French lawyer had helped him out of prison and cleared his name. I ended up with tears in my eyes. So that was Habib's story. It explained everything.

I never saw him again. Due to my constant moving around Europe I lost his phone number and address. But every time I have a shower and look at the scar on my left thigh, the memories flood back.

3

A Fatal Reward

Life in my home town was boring. I could not get any work because of my conviction back in 1967. The dreadful experience on the Libyan border had left a psychological scar on me and there was nobody I could talk to about it. The wound on my leg had not healed for a long time and I was limping. I gave up doing anything illegal.

The money that Habib had sent me was slowly disappearing. I had to pay the rent for a room in the centre of town and my car had to be taxed and insured. I had managed to acquire a new passport and went to work in Austria as a part-time mechanic. The wages were good but I could not get a work visa and therefore, my situation was precarious. I had to find a way out. The travel agencies along the Yugoslav coast were looking for Swedish and Norwegian speaking tour guides. The only way to learn those two languages fully was to work in those countries.

I had read an advert in a magazine called The Caterer and Housekeeper that said the German railways were recruiting new stewards for their forthcoming 1973 summer season. All that was required was to go and attend a language course in Norway and work at one of their designated hotels for railway stewards in order to obtain practical experience. My application was successful and within one month I was on the train to Frankfurt.

The company had recruited some sixty candidates and had made all the necessary arrangements regarding the paperwork. The group consisted of four different nationalities: Spanish, Italian, Greek and Yugoslav. The hotel was on the south

Norwegian coast very close to the town of Bergen and the language lessons were given on the hotel premises. The lessons were based on the Pitman method and we all progressed very quickly.

I was given the position of a grill chef because of my catering experience in Switzerland. The work was fun, at least at the beginning. The Norwegian waiting staff were a very friendly bunch of people, or so they seemed. The hotel's four-star grill main dishes were fillets of halibut or beef. I had to be very quick and unfortunately, in the process of learning how to keep up with fast orders, I overcooked and slightly charred many steaks which had to be given to the staff canteen. I earned the nickname Zeflon to reflect that I had a knack of burning steaks even when they were being cooked in a Teflon frying pan which was designed for the opposite. On the quiet, the hotel personnel welcomed this unexpected improvement on the staff menu! Of course, they liked the prime cut fillet steaks, even if they were slightly over well-done, but the management was not impressed.

When learning a new language, people very quickly learn all the swear words and they often end up being used inappropriately. This regularly caused much amusement and laughter. After a few months, I became reasonably fluent and progressed. I was promoted from being a grill chef to a restaurant supervisor when it was my suggestion to change the charcoal grill to a different design as a result of the many burnt steaks. The hotel management took a serious interest in my capabilities, especially in how I handled all the inevitable disputes that often occur in the catering trade.

The three month's course had come to an end and the hotel management asked me to stay on with the prospect of furthering my career at a Norwegian hotel management college. They were prepared to approach the German State Railways Company and exchange me for another candidate. The company agreed and after a few days I had been put on the hotel payroll.

My earnings were considerably higher than the waiters and I began to save whenever possible. Cigarettes and alcohol were prohibitively expensive but I soon learned through my Norwegian counterparts how to obtain many highly taxed items for a lot less from the NATO personnel and marines who often landed at one of the military bases near Bergen and would frequently enjoy themselves at our hotel.

Through the network of hotel porters and waiters, the goods, which were the marines' personal allowances, were quickly bought for Norwegian Kronas. Everybody was happy with the deal and the savings were considerable. The marines and other NATO personnel then spent the money at the hotel restaurant and the ballroom bar. Sometimes we had trouble sending these customers away at closing time. At times, fights would break out and it was extremely difficult to break up these conflicts diplomatically without calling the police. I had come from a wine drinking country and understood how alcohol can impair a person's judgement and behaviour. Luckily though, there were never any issues with drugs.

The summer was approaching and the hotel was fully

booked. There were plenty of opportunities for overtime. I was also allowed to use the hotel dance floor on my days off. I wanted to achieve my goal as soon as possible and go to a warmer country. I was open with my superiors: they knew my plans and appreciated my honesty.

I decided to buy a car. It was my dream to own a Mini Cooper; its thick middle exhaust pipe impressed me enormously. The price was a bit higher than in Austria or Germany but I saved hard for another two months.

The feeling of owning a Cooper was exhilarating. I began to explore the Norwegian countryside and the famous fjords; the views were breathtaking. In those days there was still snow visible on the mountains in the faraway distance, even though it was mid-July.

My attractive Norwegian girlfriend, whose name was Ganor, wanted me to meet her parents who lived about two hundred miles up north. We had agreed to share the cost of fuel. The journey took most of the day. Her parents were very impressed with me and at the end of our visit they asked me to come and see them again. Perhaps Ganor thought that we would eventually marry and I could stay in Norway for good. She became very possessive although I gave her no indication that the relationship was very serious. My mind was set on learning their language, working hard for a year, and then joining a Scandinavian tour operator and becoming a multilingual tour manager or rep on the Mediterranean coast.

The possessiveness began when Ganor became aware of this and eventually we parted. She worked at the same hotel as me and had become quite obstructive to my work as it had taken her a while to realise that I was determined to follow my destiny. Throughout all our courtship I hadn't told her anything about all the tragedies I had gone through in the preceding eight years.

Ganor and I made up somehow but on the understanding that our relationship was now of a platonic nature. One evening, she casually asked me if I had received my share of the gratuities which we normally split between the sixteen waiters, head-waiters and the restaurant grill bar staff every fortnight. I nodded and then she asked me if I had wondered about the latest amount which had been considerably higher than usual. I hadn't checked my last sealed envelope with the tips. I didn't need to spend any money since I had everything at the hotel. I had accommodation, food, and the hotel uniform down to my underwear. I had a bank account where my wages were paid and so had kept the envelopes mostly unopened.

I enquired whether she was implying there were mistakes in relation to my share. After fishing with more questions, she began to say things that I did not want to hear. Apparently the barmen and the waiters had been selling on some of the spirits and cigarettes supplied by the visiting military personnel as legitimate goods in our grill bar. It dawned on me that the very same, supposedly imported, duty free cigarettes and spirits had been sold to me through the bar tills at the staff discounted price as well!

I wanted to know how long this had gone on for and if she

was aware of the possible consequences. Ganor stated she had no choice but to go along with it from the moment she began work at the restaurant, especially if she wanted to keep her job.

At first I wanted to go to the hotel manager the following day and tell him about what had been going on in the restaurant bar and grill department. Intuition told me not to do that just yet. I had to find out from Ganor's confession how many people were involved in the scam - one in which I had inadvertently become implicated.

This book is not about how honest I am, but doing some ticket touting and smuggling a few pairs of jeans back to my home country was a totally different ball game to what I was facing here. I wanted to act immediately. I just could not bear to think that I would be considered a thief at the establishment that had treated me so honourably and who went out of their way to accommodate virtually my every request!

To begin with, I originally wanted to talk to my superior who was the assistant general manager of the hotel that same evening. Ganor pleaded with me not to do that because she would lose her job, along with the rest of the staff on my shift. I took pity on her and requested a meeting, via Ganor, between me, the four head-waiters and the grill chef whose role will be explained shortly.

The meeting took place the following morning at one of the neighbouring coffee bars. They could hardly look me straight in the eye. I told them in my broken Norwegian that the fraud had to stop from that moment on and that they had to go and remove all the smuggled cigarettes, spirits and anything else illegal from the grill bar shelves. I also warned them that at the next hotel stock-taking, the truth could come out and that they would have to bear the consequences.

I took the envelope out of my back pocket that contained my share of the tips received in the past fortnight and handed it over to one of the head-waiters who appeared to be their leader. My words were: "I am out of something that I had no knowledge of ever being in. Nor did I agree to be part of any sort of ring which is rotten to the core."

One of the head-waiters began sizing me up. I didn't hesitate to tell him that I wasn't afraid to talk to them as bluntly as I had and that he and the rest of his gang should think very hard about their future. I warned him that sooner or later their activities would come to the hotel management's attention. I politely told them that all I wanted was to complete my studies and protect my integrity for the duration of my stay in their country. I also assured them that I had no intention of rocking the boat as long as they did not try to suck me into their little game.

My conditions were accepted. I again demanded that all the duty free items be immediately removed from the grill bar and that I would check every order that came out of the kitchen during my shift. Deep down, I worried whether I was doing the right thing but I took a chance in not informing the management, at least for the next twenty-four hours.

I then stood up and assured them that for the next few

days I would not say a word to anyone. Ganor felt the whole thing appeared too good to be true. I soon figured out that she had told me the truth. They had been doing all this stealing and smuggling well before my arrival. I accepted the fact that it would be foolish for me as an outsider, having been in the country for five minutes and leaving in a few months time, to speak out and challenge their behaviour.

Because of my managerial position, in the eyes of the law I would have been found equally guilty of fraud as they were for not having informed head office about the ongoing misconduct. With that in view, the scales in any subsequent court proceeding would have probably been tipped against me. I thought that it would be best to wait and see how things developed but gave them the ultimatum to carry out my demands within twenty-four hours. As for the words "not rock the boat", they haunt me to this day.

At the same time, I lost all respect for Ganor. Had I wished to go down the route of criminality I had already had plenty of offers to do so. Even when I worked in Switzerland there had been a variety of propositions made to me such as smuggling diamonds and gold obtained in Switzerland to different parts of the world. I would have none of it.

After the meeting with the grill staff and the head-waiters, I took a few days off, possibly because of the pressure I found myself under. Ganor kept me informed about the stock that had to be removed from the shelves and my demands were followed to the letter: all smuggled items were removed completely. When I returned to do my shift I immediately checked the shelves to see whether the stock had been changed. To my surprise all the stuff that wasn't supposed to be there in the first place had gone! I had expected the head-waiters to try and 'pull another fast one' on me.

I also realised that I had no alternative but to stop buying any cigarettes 'on the cheap' so as not to give the staff any reason to compromise me. I hadn't taken any share of the tips either just to be on the safe side. I sensed that it would only be a matter of time before the restaurant and grill bar staff came up with another trick. And they did.

Over the following days, the grill chef stopped collecting the counter dockets for the food that came out of the kitchen grill between 2pm and 4pm, keeping the takings for himself. The shift change at that time enabled the head-waiters to find another way to line their pockets. I had to turn a blind eye for the next two days for the simple reason that I needed to find out how to solve this problem. It felt to me as though I was trying to stop water running through a sieve.

There was another reason for me not to immediately intervene. Ganor had warned me that the staff on my shift were planning a walk out on one of the busiest days which was Friday. I also realised that Ganor felt spurned and therefore had no sympathy for me, believing that one day I would tell the management what had been going on. I concluded that eventually I would be forced to leave.

At that stage, I hadn't accepted any more shares of the tips whatsoever. I am in no way trying to portray all Norwegian people as dishonest, but the people I worked with unfortunately were - the whole bunch of them. I didn't know what to do next. My plans to finish the Norwegian course were seemingly in tatters. I still didn't want to go to the management because that would only aggravate the whole situation and speed up my departure. But equally I could no longer tolerate the shortcomings at the tills. If I didn't say anything to the grill chef, there wouldn't be anything left in the tills for the next hour of my shift. I had been put into a desperate situation and there was only one option left to me. I asked the waiters' gang leader to again meet me at the same coffee shop where we had had our first meeting a few days earlier. He agreed and the two of us met the next day.

I came straight to the point. I demanded that he and the rest of his gang stop thieving from the kitchen. If they wanted to steal from the hotel coffers they should find another way of doing so, as long as it wasn't done on my watch. I looked straight into his eyes and said that if I was forced to leave my post, the management would be informed with some hard facts about their activities and that this would be done long after I had gone. I added that it was not my fault that their little game was interrupted by me and that he and his gang should consider themselves very lucky that I hadn't already reported them to the management.

"What would you do if I had to leave and another supervisor or restaurant manager took over?" I asked Hedar. "What would a new manager do in my position?" He just looked at me and I could see again how surprised he was by my frankness. He promised that he would do everything possible not to make me look responsible for any impropriety during my shift. I warned him that the auditors would one day find out about all the shortcomings. He and the rest of his crew would pay for it and there would be no need for them to think about who had tipped them off. I shook his hand believing that I had saved my planned stay and hoped that all their activities would come out long after I had left.

The grill chef towed the line and I did not detect any wrongdoing for the next month. The till takings were back to normal, at least on my shift. I began to correspond with a worldwide agency. The Swiss Kuoni travel agency was looking for a Norwegian speaking representative for the following year on the Adriatic coast, possibly in Dubrovnik. If I fulfilled their requirements they were willing to employ me in Switzerland during the winter season. The future looked good.

The hotel management had arranged a picnic for all the personnel on a small island not far from Bergen as a token of gratitude for a very good season. We were all excited and looked forward to it. I hoped that it would improve the morale and performance of the staff and possibly change their attitude as regards to the restaurant's shortcomings. I had decided that I would leave my post as manager very soon. After all, the season had come slowly to an end and my course was nearing the final exams. The daylight was still nearly eighteen hours long but, according to the natives, the long winter nights were slowly creeping upon us.

Ganor and I drove to the small port on the outskirts of

Bergen and waited with some of the other hotel employees to cross the narrow sea strait to the small island which was a mere three hundred or so yards away. There were about fifteen small speed boats provided to ferry us across to the island. As is normal for occasions like this, people around me had already drunk some alcohol beforehand but that did not bother me at the time since the boat operators did not show any signs of indulging in the same.

The atmosphere on the island was great. I didn't even know that there were so many people working at the hotel. Some had brought their spouses' along as well. I reckoned that there were about a hundred and twenty people in all. There were mountains of food and almost unlimited supplies of drink. It was a warm and sunny day which was unusual for Bergen. I couldn't remember a day when it had not rained there. There were a few jokes about my running the restaurant bar at the neighbouring tables but I was avoiding engaging too much in any deep discussion about the way I ran the business.

I could hear the compliments about my catering and Swiss-style book-keeping. One of the waitresses had quite openly said that the hotel needed someone like me. She had very nearly said out loud that the department which I was in charge of needed someone as honest as me and all around her knew exactly what she was saying. I felt embarrassed and had to say something to diffuse the situation because of the management presence. I commented in a few words that things overall weren't so bad. I had not drunk any of the alcohol and tried to warn the waitress not to talk too much.

Of course she'd had one too many already and we had the whole evening ahead. I begged her not to say anything more about it during the dance. I went to the dance floor a few times and took to one of the female receptionists.

My now ex-girlfriend Ganor became very jealous and began to drink more and more. Suddenly, out of the blue I had a problem on my hands. I decided to use my tact and took her to the dance floor a few times until, in the end, she fell asleep on one of the benches. My instincts told me not to get too close to the receptionist for the time being in case Ganor woke up and caused an ugly scene.

We had a disco, a karaoke and a small band. I played a bit on the organ and was awarded with applause. I wasn't an attention seeker but I wanted to show that we Yugoslavs were cultured as well!

After nearly five hours of marathon drinking and eating, I noticed that some of the female personnel had lost all of their inhibitions. I had foreseen this because I had experienced it myself many times back in my own country. Had it not been for Ganor, I might have tried to hook up with the young ladies that were single like me.

The time passed ever so quickly and by 10.30pm there was still daylight. Despite people stumbling over each other, there had not been not a single argument amongst the, by now, rather tipsy personnel. There was laughter to be heard coming from all corners. The Nordic race can drink a lot and still retain a clear-eyed look, whereas southern Europeans' eyes appear to become bloodshot when drunk.

The whole picnic must have cost thousands so the hotel had evidently had a very good season. One of the managers quietly told me that there was a surprise waiting for me on my next pay day and that I should not leave them. If only he knew the real reason for me leaving. On top of the myriad problems with the staff, I had never really liked the snow and temperatures below fifteen degrees Celsius. The coming long winter nights did not appeal to me either. This attitude might have stemmed from my childhood since my father had always forced me to wear my brother's old worn out clothes in which I felt the cold. But the other reason was that I was worried that it would only take an auditor's quick look at the books and the financial shortcomings of the bar and grill would come to light. Although not all aspects of the restaurant were under my control, I would still have to answer for some things. I simply had to go. Period.

It was getting close to midnight and we began preparing to leave the little island. I must have been the only one who was completely sober. The speedboats had made their first few trips to the shore and I reckoned that it would take a good while before everybody reached the other side. Each boat could take nine of the one hundred and twenty people at a time.

I wasn't in any hurry and wanted to help poor Ganor in order to bring her safely back to the hotel. Most of the employees lived at the hotel. I knew that this was not done out of the good heart of the hotel management but simply so that they could call on us at any given moment.

A Fatal Reward

A group of us - fifteen from the restaurant - were waiting to be taken to the small harbour where I had parked my car. The person in charge of the speedboat that Ganor and I were allocated to smelt of alcohol so I held Ganor back and tried to tell her that we should wait for the next boat. Because of her drunken stupor, she kept insisting we go on the boat that was waiting for us. However, when the next boat came I pushed Ganor into it.

The captain of the first boat, who had visibly had one drink too many, offered me a place in his boat. The second boat, in which Ganor sat half slumped on the boat's bench, had a space for another person but as I tried to leave the first boat with its drunken skipper, it jerked forward and began to cast off.

I had a kind of premonition that something was about to happen. Fully dressed in my suit, I jumped overboard and swam towards the second boat which was still waiting back at the dock. The water was ice cold and I would not have lasted long in it. The skipper and the half-drunk passengers in the second vessel looked at me with disbelief as they plucked me out of the water into the boat, commenting on my courage and saying that it was a silly thing to do.

After about a minute, I began to shiver and people gave me items of their clothing to replace my wet ones. Ganor kept saying that I looked just like James Bond in one of his films. I looked ahead and said to her that I had a feeling that we might see a real life drama at any moment. The skipper in the first boat had waited for us, only to begin a little game of dare with our skipper. As he came closer to us I noticed that he had two people too many on board and that the boat was on the brink of taking in water. Our skipper overtook the first boat and headed for harbour.

The skipper of the first boat tried then to overtake us in return but one of its two powerful engines had failed and the boat began to veer away gaining speed and heading directly towards the granite wave breakers. I shouted: "Look out, look out!" but the first boat continued its curved course towards the breakers with considerable speed. Then, all we saw was the boat shooting into the air and people falling onto the boulders.

Before we could reach the point of the crash, there were four or five other boats already at the scene trying to rescue two of the passengers who were trapped under the capsized, sinking vessel. Tragically, three people died and the skipper ended up paralysed. Ironically both of the passengers who had taken the places meant for Ganor and me were two of the fatalities. Unfortunately the third person killed on that tragic day was Hedar.

I was asked to testify against the skipper but opted not to do so. In my mind I did not want to be a victim of possible reprisals. There were enough other witnesses and I was exonerated from any involvement.

2

A Flight to the Death

In the immediate aftermath of that dreadful boat tragedy I decided to give in my notice but the hotel management pleaded with me to stay on. As I explained before, it was very difficult for me to give them the real reasons for the decision which were two-fold. Not only had I got to come to terms with the loss of life of three people, if I stayed, I would also have the ongoing problem with the staff regarding their improprieties. I simply couldn't tell them the truth. I was given a generous 'goodbye' severance payment and an excellent reference.

Meanwhile I had to complete my language course and find new employment. The season had come to an end and I had to accept a post at a fast-food processing plant, about eighty miles up north. It was a totally new type of work but I quickly settled into the new environment despite the fact the wages were much lower.

I planned to stay on at least until the following spring when my Norwegian would be good enough to have another go at being a tour guide on the Croatian coast. The people I worked with were very different to most of those back at the hotel. I felt privileged to be amongst such hard working and honest people. The whole time I worked there, I felt as though I was part of a large family. We had laughs and lots of company parties. The time working there passed very quickly.

One amusing thing was the native home brewing which reminded me of my own home where we used to brew and distil our own beer and spirits. On a few occasions I got quite intoxicated and, as any young man would, I had a few short-term relationships but nothing serious. Had Norway geographically been somewhere in the Mediterranean, I would most certainly have stayed there for good.

The Kuoni Swiss Travel Agency had offered me a post somewhere on the Italian coast but after conditions were set out, I decided that it wasn't the right thing to do. I politely turned down their offer and reopened negotiations with my old agency in Dubrovnik. My so-called friend Joseph wasn't there any longer and I had one more language under my belt. My sins were forgiven and forgotten by them.

So, at the beginning of spring 1975, I followed through with my plans and returned to Dubrovnik. The old tour company took me back straight away and gave me spacious accommodation very close to the centre of the old town. The tragic accident two years previously was seldom mentioned and I quickly regained my popularity. I was one of the few who spoke Norwegian and the company saw me as an asset.

But my destiny took its own course.

My tour operator had various tour programs and one of these was the 'fish picnic'. An old passenger steam ship would take some two hundred tourists to one of the small islands not far from Dubrovnik for the day. The food and drinks would be included in the price of the excursion. I was asked to conduct one of these tours. I was to be in charge of Norwegian and German speaking groups. The other groups had their own designated guides.

It started off perfectly. Guests began to drink the strong

local red wine that was flowing freely at the ship's bar. In no time I could see that it was already having an effect on people's behaviour and I felt an urge to inform the other tour guides that there might be some problems ahead regarding the safety of our passengers. My suggestions were dismissed as being too cautious and a bit paranoid.

I had to resort to using the radio communication between the steamer and my HQ in Dubrovnik to inform them about possible accidents due to too much alcohol being served too soon without any food. One of the German guests, in his alcoholic stupor, wanted to make love with one of the drunken American ladies inside the life boat and, wait for it, they asked me to open the heavy canvas for them to climb in! After a lengthy conversation with my agency, they agreed to trust my judgement and ordered the captain to stop serving any more alcohol until we reached the island.

As a result, I was immediately ridiculed and told that I should have spoken to the captain first. But to illustrate that I had acted responsibly, my communication with the head office was made in the captain's control room in his presence. The behaviour of the whole crew was stupid and irresponsible. I went as far as calling them "idiots who were too drunk themselves not to see the dangers that possibly lay ahead "!

We finally reached the island and were heading towards the small harbour when I noticed with apprehension that most of our guests were already very drunk. They cheered and looked with excitement at the tables and benches laid out at the end of the jetty.

What horrified me was that there were no waiters or chefs to greet us. The steamer began to dock and I noticed that two of our passengers had jumped into the water and were attempting to swim ahead of the ship in order to impress their friends. But there seemed to be no way that these two drunk passengers would be able to get out of the water before the steamer reached them and, almost certainly, crush them against the wall of the jetty!

Moments passed and I realised that the captain was not aware of this situation. I rushed through the deck towards the captain's cabin and shouted out the imminent danger. One of the officers grabbed a long pole with a hook attached to it, ran to the side of the ship and plucked the two drunks one by one out of the water. A few moments later, the steamer touched the jetty walls. It was a very, very close call!

As we disembarked, the other tour guides were rallying around me asking how I was able to foresee these events happening. I gave them a very honest answer, that a person didn't have to be a clairvoyant to foresee things like this. In this case, the simple answer was 'alcohol in their brains'. As for my ability to foresee the future, they didn't need to worry because I had no magic wand - I couldn't even foresee my own future let alone any one else's.

That was not the end of the catalogue of errors and calamities that followed. The promised food arrived very late in the afternoon and by then, the passengers had drunk so much wine and other alcoholic drinks that most of the food was left uneaten. I have never witnessed anything like it before. It was total mayhem and I really regretted being on that excursion at all.

By late afternoon, because of an approaching storm, the captain ordered that we had to embark as quickly as possible. But at the last count we were still missing two people. After a lengthy search, we had no choice but to leave them behind and set sail before the storm could reach us on our return home.

Most of the drunken passengers were lying on the deck chairs and a lot of them were violently sick. Halfway across on the journey back, we encountered a very rough and choppy sea. Two grossly overweight people who were resting on deck chairs in the aft of the ship, were rocked out of them and started to tumble in my direction. From where I stood, I could see some twenty yards down the galley. The ship's hull was lifting and then slamming back into the waves. Suddenly, there was chaos in the seating areas and everything that wasn't fixed to the floor was flying all over the place. I had to decide whether to shut the double swing doors and let these two huge body masses smash themselves to a pulp or to open the doors and let these roly-poly passengers through them towards the stern of the ship. I went for the second option.

I swiftly opened the huge doors so that they wouldn't crash into them and at the same time not flatten me. I was later told by another Italian speaking tour guide how he had seen me as some kind of Spanish matador opening the fly doors and letting those poor ladies roll past me. I was the talk of the month.

However, I was certainly not amused and felt sorry for what had happened. The head of the company sided with my version of events. There was really no other way out for me in that situation. Sadly the two passengers suffered a few broken ribs. One American lady broke both her legs and in total there were ten people taken to hospital on our arrival at Dubrovnik harbour. The management wanted to know why the crew and the captain had not listened to my advice sooner.

I went to visit the injured almost every day. The head office made sure that a taxi took me there and they offered the casualties every assistance. I had to translate all the paperwork that was needed for their insurance company back in the USA. I offered to do the work for free but they insisted I was paid.

It was all settled out of court and there was only one interview with the local police. I couldn't criticise my company's conduct too much. The cruises stopped for a few weeks and had to be rescheduled. All possible safety measures were installed before they were reinstated. Of course, I made it clear to my company that there would be no way that I would take another group to any fish picnic again.

After most of the injured passengers were discharged from the hospital, I asked the management if I could be transferred to one of the nearby islands, Corcula. They agreed to this, sympathising with my position. Here, there was less hassle and I had more time for myself. The wages were the same and it suited me fine. I noticed, thank God, that I became much calmer. There was a Swedish SAS (Swedish Airline System) based on the island and I would tour with their clients around the island and the whole of Yugoslavia.

On one of these tours, I met a young lady by the name of Susan who came from Chesham in the UK. We saw each other daily and I quite liked her. She told me about her unhappy relationship which had ended a few months before she came to the island. Meanwhile, I had found a letter addressed to me in our agency's despatch room that dated back two years from the Westinghouse Travel Company with various offers of employment in the USA. I phoned them immediately and the same people I had met previously were still there. I even spoke to the same person who had asked me more than two years ago to join their team.

Mr Balon said that he had been very impressed with my knowledge of what they needed and how professionally I had served them as a waiter, tour manager, and pianist. They promised that they would speak to me within the next few days and arrange all the paperwork needed including flight tickets and a working visa for the USA. I was thrilled. I told Susan that my plans were to go to the US and that she shouldn't take our relationship seriously. As she left, I promised her that I would keep in touch and all the various things that I used to say to other girls since, deep down, I knew that after a few weeks, their memory of what I said would fizzle out and all my promises would be forgotten.

Susan appeared to be in love with me, at least, that's what she kept telling me in her letters and phone calls. She asked me to come to England and said that we could have a wonderful life in London. I wouldn't have any problems finding a decent job in the thriving hotel industry and that she could care for me while I was waiting for permission to work in the UK. She mentioned marriage but I was not ready for it.

The season soon ended in Corcula. I had made my mind up to travel to the US. Westinghouse had arranged all the necessary paperwork and the flight tickets were to be collected at the American embassy in Amsterdam. I told Susan that I would not come to England after all. Susan was very persistent and asked me to wait for her in Amsterdam where we could talk it over. I must confess that I admired her persistence and decided to wait for her there. My plane ticket was valid for another week after Susan's arrival so I had nothing to lose.

When she arrived, I was promised that after a year or so of living together we could both try our luck in the US. I felt bad for Mr Balon and the Westinghouse Corporation in letting them down. I phoned them from Chesham and they were very upset. Susan kept her promise as regards my upkeep but after three months I made her sit down and listen to me. She had realised that I wasn't very happy being a kept man and that my money was, as before, dwindling very fast.

I made a plan to leave the next morning after she had gone to work. She must have sensed this and rang me an hour later from her work place, telling me to wait for her to return from work. Again we had a long talk and she asked me to marry her. I told her that although I loved her, there were not enough reasons for us to get married. She then asked me if I would like to do some work at an upmarket pub whose landlady she knew. I jumped at the idea and questioned why she hadn't suggested it before. Her answer surprised me: she feared that I would run away with another woman.

I should have thought about those words very carefully. After a month or so, she asked me again if I would marry her. I considered it for a while and said yes. After all, she had showed that she loved me and she had been very careful with her money: she had two jobs and was paying her own mortgage. I was very confident that within a year I would earn enough money to have my own mortgage and everything would be 'hunky dory'.

After we married I was offered a position as restaurant manager at a Holiday Inn in Slough not far from our home. But there was so much pilfering going on, I couldn't sustain the position. Twenty-six 1lb packs of bacon went missing on my first working day! I had to go and wake up a butcher early in the morning to give me some bacon so that the cooks could prepare the English breakfasts. I finally realised that there is a global problem within the catering industry whereby the staff simply steal from the kitchens, bars and cold stores etc.

I decided I wanted to work in London as a live-in manager. Susan would be able to rent out her property in Chesham and live with me. Unfortunately cracks in our marriage had begun to appear. I was wrongly accused of adultery and unfortunately she caused some ugly scenes in front of paying guests. Her jealousy resulted in a rift between me and my employers. Susan's interference in my running of the hotel became a problem.

Following various subsequent posts and after three years of marriage, we went our separate ways. I took it as a defeat but saw nothing wrong with my attitude during our marriage. She just couldn't understand that the catering industry, and especially running a hotel, is a twenty-four seven, three hundred and sixty-five days a year job. I also had to travel to different workshops to promote the particular hotel I was working for.

In March 1980, I successfully passed the exams to become a driving instructor. It was a very interesting time in my life. There were situations when a pupil would suddenly change direction and didn't have any explanation for why he or she did it. I am sure that I probably did the same when I started. There were also many instances when my pupils would begin to panic, for example in the middle of Hyde Park Corner roundabout after stubbornly insisting on a drive through central London before they were ready. This was often due to them being over confident and misleading me as to their true ability, not being aware of my duty of care to them.

Often, they had already had some fifty to sixty lessons with different driving schools. Despite having dual controls, the steering wheel was in their hands and sometimes I had to grab it on a dual carriageway in order to prevent an accident. Strangely enough, as I mentioned before, I didn't see or feel that my life was in danger at all! In all the five years of being an instructor I can state that I didn't have an accident while teaching. Of course, there is a certain element of luck involved.

Naturally, I fell for one of my pupils and remarried but the long hours being on the road as an instructor did our marriage no good. After a year I was single again. I could tell a lot of stories about driving instructors and their pupils but I stuck to my code of honour and never got involved while my female pupils were learning how to pass their driving test. I had a few flings but only after a pupil had passed their test successfully.

After a while I decided to work as an independent driving instructor and concentrated on teaching female pupils in automatic cars. Very soon I was in the position of employing another instructor. Within a year I bought a flat in a very affluent and leafy part of Notting Hill Gate. Somehow my life was taking a course that I wanted except for one thing, I longed for a family of my own.

Every approved driving instructor must also pass an additional test for the Department of Transport examiner to show their ongoing competence to teach. There is also a limited number of lessons that an instructor can teach on a working day. Any criminal offence renders the instructor's licence void immediately. As far as I am aware, there are only three penalty points allowed on the instructor's personal driving licence. On one competence test, the examiner, who had my history of lessons in his dossier, made a remark that he had only known of a small number of instructors with no accidents whatsoever. He even didn't conclude the test since my records showed that I was very competent. I am not trying to brag but I know when I am good at something. I have also been bad on quite a few occasions in my life but I see this as part of the normal process in someone's progress.

The examiner, whose name was Oliver, made the suggestion that I would be an ideal candidate as a flight instructor due to my multi-tasking abilities. I took him seriously and made some enquiries at an airfield near Watford in Hertfordshire. The lessons were very pricey but I went ahead and booked a trial lesson at Leavesden Airfield near Garston. My future instructor was very honest with me and told me that it was impossible to guarantee my success, but nevertheless I should try at least one half-hour lesson.

I liked it immediately. The next thing for me to do was to obtain a medical certificate from a Civil Aviation Authority-authorised medical examiner. I passed and was issued with a medical certificate class two and three. There were a mountain of subjects to be learnt by heart. Within three hours my instructor had advised me that I should continue and possibly after a few months qualify for a private pilot licence.

The theory taught at flying school was very difficult. There was no time to ask questions regarding the different expressions and abbreviations which were all in English. English is the only language spoken in aeronautics and there are no personal translators available up in the air. The pilots and navigators have to be conversant in English in order to follow the directions, weather reports, and countless information being given during the pre-flight, take-off and landing procedures.

A Flight to the Death

I was determined to become a flight instructor. I stayed at my flying school based at High Wycombe flight centre for hours on end and studied all the videos about meteorology, navigation and every aspect of flying. Flying took over my life until I had my first solo flight.

Upon my arrival at the school that day, I still vividly remember that some of the instructors came to my table in the refreshment area and tried to strike up a conversation with me. One of them asked me about using a forward slip at landing and a lot of other questions. I know now that they just wanted to make sure that I was competent enough to fly my first solo flight. At that point I didn't know that it was the final briefing before it.

My instructor took me to the plane and I was given the control, meaning that the instructor was leaving it to me to do all the pre-flight checks that are needed every time before a take-off. The engine was set to normal revving. As I put my foot on the brakes and increased the necessary revs of the engine before the 'roll', my instructor suddenly opened his door and jumped out, saying in a loud voice:

"Zdenko, whatever your religion is you are now on your own and I will see you in while." He then shut the door and walked briskly off the tarmac.

In no time I took off. The feeling of being on your own in the air is indescribable! I felt great and was proud of myself at being able to achieve something many people only dream about. After half an hour of circling over the airport, I had to concentrate on how to land safely. The take-off and flying an aeroplane can be learnt quite quickly but to land safely is an incredible task. Many would-be pilots have never accomplished this part.

I booked some further lessons and soon realised that in order to qualify as a flying instructor, all my savings would go on the lessons. After a lengthy search, I found a flight academy in Florida. The lessons in the UK had cost me an average of seventy-five pounds each, but in the US, the lessons would only cost me twenty dollars all inclusive. I booked a package holiday to Miami that included car hire. My thirty flying hours at the Florida Flight Academy, accommodation near the school, the return flight and car hire cost me four hundred and seventy pounds in total - a considerable saving.

I arrived in the USA for my first lesson and my designated flight instructor took me up in the air to see how prepared I was for my FAA (Federal Aviation Authority) practice test. He gave me control of the plane and I began the simulated emergency landing procedure. He seemed to be very impressed by my handling. I found the ideal spot for landing and at the altitude of 150 feet aborted the simulated landing since the simulated emergency landing is what it means. Simulated. According to his report back at the school, I would have landed more tightly on that chosen field than he had thought possible.

My flight school informed me that I would have to fly at least three times a day in order to be able to book my 'check' ride with the very busy examiner. I had almost eighteen days left to prepare myself for the examination. In those days the theoretical test was done previously on the computer. There were only three attempts allowed per session. I passed on my first attempt.

My one fear was my communication ability over the radio. All the controllers spoke in heavy American accents to which I had to listen very carefully. The days passed and my 'check' ride - in reality a practical test - was approaching very fast. The examiner was very pleasant and spoke with a soft American voice which I understood. After about an hour in the air, he asked me to return to Punta Garda. I asked him whether I had failed because he hadn't asked me to perform an emergency landing. He replied, with a smile on his face, that he had read about my flying progress very carefully and he hadn't had any need to ask me about that since I had shown myself to be competent enough to fly solo in future!

Bingo! I was over the moon. I still had a week left of my holiday and had been given five free flying hours 'on the house'. I booked a further five hours flying time just to practise enough to be able to pass the UK practical exams. I was, in a sense, a qualified private pilot but I could not take any passengers on board until I had a PPL (private pilot's licence) certificate sent to me.

The flight academy had offered me a post as a flight instructor if I passed the practical exams in the IFR category. IFR stands for Instruments Flight Rules meaning that the pilot can fly in almost all weather conditions using the navigation instruments that the plane is equipped with. The wages would have been much lower than those I had earned back in the UK. I now had a junk shop which after tax earned me enough money to go on holiday twice a year. With the wages of being a flight instructor in the US, I would lose all that. However on the continent, for example in Germany, the going rate for an instructor was one hundred and twenty-five pounds per hour.

My expectations were somewhat dampened. I would have to be at least rated as a twin engine flight instructor in order to make a decent living and to do that, I would again have to pass the CPL (commercial pilot licence) examination. At any stage I could lose all of that should my medical condition change for the worse: high blood pressure, dental problems or any possible ailments would mean I could lose my licence. However, at that moment I had only one immediate thing on my mind - to do as many hours as possible and achieve goal number two, the UK PPL.

I flew all over southern Florida from Fort Meyers to Marcos Island, from Lakeland to Boca Raton and many other places. On one of the short distance solo flights, the plane's engine stopped all of a sudden, probably due to adulterated fuel. I managed to bring the plane with its engine spluttering back to the base. I didn't feel any nervousness throughout the small ordeal. The flight academy had one more reason to keep me there.

I carefully logged all my flight hours but unfortunately, one of my flight log books went missing at some point over the years. But I am still in possession of the log book which illustrates the sequence of the following events that led me to another near disaster.

On the fateful day of 11th December 1993, I had hired a Cessna 152 to do another solo cross country flight from Punta Garda to a district airport at Lakeland, one hundred and twenty miles up north. I filed my flight plan which is in case of emergencies whereby search and rescue services are automatically notified following non-arrival at the given time at a given airport. The weather report showed no adverse conditions and I took off in the planned direction. The time was exactly 11am. I planned to climb up to three thousand feet where I would level out, and at a constant speed continue towards Lakeland. The engine sounded okay and all the instruments were showing that the plane was on its course.

After about half an hour I noticed that my plane was veering to the right. There are a few basic instruments that are installed on every plane. The more powerful and faster planes, such as jets, have a myriad of instruments beside the basic ones. My Cessna was equipped with an altimeter,(which indicated through barometric pressure mechanism the height) airspeed indicator (which indicates how fast the plane travels through the air,) attitude indicator, heading indicator, vertical speed indicator (which indicates the speed of descent or a climb), magnetic compass, direction indicator, engine revs and engine temperature indicators. There also is a flap control switch, transponder switches, VOR instruments and the radio control switches. I won't go into the whole palaver necessary for me to be in the cockpit but this is just to give you a basic idea of what is needed to fly and stay up in the air.

Every single pilot, be it a supersonic pilot or a Jet Harrier pilot, had to go through a basic single engine training program. People are not always aware that even a Concorde pilot would have trained and practised this way before moving on to the sadly decommissioned jet. As my plane was veering to the right, my VOR needle was beginning to move uncontrollably from right to left. VOR stands for Very high frequency Omni radio signal or Omni radial. It is an instrument that is used by pilots to find their bearings relative to the VOR station, normally situated near airports. Today it is mainly used by smaller aircraft while airliners use GPS technology although they still follow VOR signals as well. In the case of autopilot being engaged, the electronics then take over what is needed to fly the charted course. One VOR station covers one leg or a portion of a flown distance and the pilot can tune into the next VOR station which is identifiable through Morse code and is calibrated for magnetic north.

I must stress that the VOR signals only tell the pilot what his position is on that radial. The radial 'rose' is divided into three hundred and sixty degrees. The VOR station is unmanned and does not know or care where the pilot is. Again it only tells the pilot whether the plane is flying towards the VOR station or away from it. It does not know the speed, height or course of the plane. It is up to the pilot to compute the course according to the signal. And it was that erratic movement of the VOR indicator needle that began to worry me. Although I had on my chart a lot of 'fixing' points along which I could fly, the VOR was needed in case I deviated from those fixes.

According to my flight plan and the DME (distance measuring equipment) I was beginning to bear quite a lot off course. My magnetic compass on the dashboard had shown a fifteen degree deviation from the direction indicator. The next thing I noticed was that the radio went off. After checking the circuit breakers were okay, I was puzzled. I could no longer hear the familiar crackling voices.

The battery charger showed no charge which meant that I would very soon be forced to switch off the rest of the electrical equipment. I then wondered how, with all the equipment switched off, I would be able to squawk into the next VOR to correct my direction.

The whole cabin became quieter and the air in the cabin started to get very humid and hazy which I put down to condensation. I could hardly see further than a few miles ahead. I had never panicked in my life and didn't intend to do so on this occasion but I was concerned at how I would communicate with the small airport that was marked on my flight plan in case of emergency, and which I presumed lay a few miles ahead. Were there any other planes in my path? I tried in vain to bring the radio back to life.

My altimeter showed an altitude well over the planned one. I decided to make a turn to avoid flying over the small airfield. The mist had cleared enough for me to see through the windshield more clearly. I tried to switch on the transponder - it came on and so did the radio. But the altimeter was showing a very high reading. I knew that at any moment the fuel carburettor would start to slow down the engine because the mixture would be too rich. I had to lean the mixture, meaning that I had to reduce the flow of fuel to the carburettor so that it was just right for the higher altitude. But what was this force that was taking me higher than four thousand feet and how long would it go on for?

My hands were trying to push the control column forward but it was simply not responding. I felt as though I was paralysed. I suspected that I must have flown through some clouds and the 'icing' was preventing me from operating the controls - and that maybe it was my imagination that I could not move any of my limbs. Just thinking about what to do seemed to take ages. I was aware of hypoxia but I wasn't high enough for it to set in.

Again the plane had begun to veer to the left. I was baffled and confused. Nothing like it had been taught at school and I tried to reduce the power to an idling position but my hands would not move. The plane was still not descending. I had no feeling in my hands but saw no need to try the radio because the radio would not bring me to a lower altitude. I was frantically trying to think clearly and attempted to make small hand movements.

I managed to slowly move my right hand towards the throttle and was able to decrease the revs to a minimum. The air speed indicator was showing me a speed of eighty knots. The plane seemed to float on some kind of giant invisible cushion or so it felt. I still had no fear and followed the instructor's teaching to the letter, that in the event of an electrical or any major failure, the most important thing is to fly the plane and to look for a spot to make an emergency landing.

I realised that at any moment the plane could stall and I wouldn't be able to do anything. I just could not move and all my physical strength had vanished. All sorts of explanations were racing through my mind. Was I being influenced by possible UFO forces? Where were they? Why couldn't I see them? I had read a lot of stories about the Bermuda Triangle but had believed those stories to be apocryphal. As I tried to dismiss all the theories about parallel universes, 'are we living in a holographic universe?' and the rest, my mind was telling me that the most important thing was to bring the plane down to the ground as safely as possible. I looked down to see whether there was a railway line that I could use as a navigation aid. Logically I should then be able to find my way back to Punta Garda. But there weren't any tracks to be seen.

It suddenly dawned on me that I was hopelessly lost and in the grip of some unknown force that was preventing me from losing height. I felt my heart beating fast but my hearing and vision were functioning normally. The radio was coming to life for a few seconds, only to disappear again. I noticed the DI (direction indicator) was showing that the plane was heading north but having been a Scout in my younger years, I did not trust either of the compasses for the simple reason that the sun was on my right hand side and I must therefore be heading south regardless of what the instruments were telling me.

Suddenly I was able to pitch the plane downwards. Hurray! Finally I had regained control of the plane. The engine was giving out some loud detonations and I immediately enriched the mixture. I gently pushed the control column forward to lose height and it was responding! As I checked the rate of descent on my instrument, it did not indicate any descent. I knew however that as long as I felt that the plane was descending I would be able to find the nearest speck of ground where I could land. All of a sudden, the radio came alive and I tried to tune into the radio frequency of my air traffic controllers. I could hear them but they couldn't hear me.

My VOR readings made no sense. The needle was swinging again from left to right as if it were some kid's toy. There was one thing that I was sure of. The engine on my plane had a magneto and as long the magneto did not overheat, the engine would run for ever. The magneto is, in a sense, a generator that is powered by the movement of the pistons and does not need battery power. As long as the cylinders had a supply of fuel, the engine would power the magneto and the magneto would supply the high voltage charge to the spark plugs which would then ignite the fuel mixture in the combustion chamber. The cycle would repeat itself. I was totally aware that in the circumstances, I had to land the plane since I didn't know what my exact position was and that other planes who could be at the same altitude didn't know about my presence.

I wondered what forces had held me up at that high

altitude and caused the total loss of electrical supply. The engine sounded all right and the airspeed indicator showed a reading that appeared to be correct. All the lessons and teaching I had had about icing had made no sense in the scenario I found myself in. My experiences as a novice pilot were not enough to analyse the fluke situation that had occurred a few minutes previously. Instinct told me to concentrate on the emergency landing as soon as possible.

There were a lot of small airfields dotted on the map en-route back to Boca Rattan and I would have to land at one of those. I kept looking at the map and controls to see if that strange experience a few minutes earlier was about to be repeated. I checked and double checked the compass on the dashboard. It showed me that I was heading in a south-westerly direction. In the far distance I could see the jet planes at low altitude coming in to land at Miami Airport and I concluded that my present course was perpendicular to the path of those jet planes. It flashed through my mind that I was not totally lost after all and that I could probably make it back to my airport without an emergency landing. I tried to find the frequency on my radio but had forgotten the number and code. My unexplained experience had left me with only three objectives: the first was to fly the plane; the second was to avoid possible collision; and the third was to bring myself and the plane safely back to the original plotted course and return to Boca Rattan.

I lowered the nose and reduced the power in order to descend to three thousand feet. There were no other planes to be seen. Then a voice came on to my earphones and asked me for identification. The transponder was showing the Miami air traffic control my presence on their screen but I could not speak or answer their questions. The frequency was unknown to them although I didn't have any recollection of ever having tuned in to that particular frequency. My memory had almost gone.

The survival instinct cut in again. I kept looking for the railway line which was my original marker. I spotted it and immediately felt better. I decided to descend for a further one thousand feet in order to follow the railway line towards my next fix or marker. My eyes caught the interior clock dial showing the time and in my mind it was impossible! It showed that I had been in the air for no longer than an hour. According to my calculations I should have been in the air for at least an hour and thirty minutes. The tank showed consumption for about an hour. How could this be? I had lost half an hour somewhere on the flight towards Lakeland. I began to doubt my capabilities to calculate the time. Again and again I checked the fuel remaining, the time on my watch and the distance that I had flown.

Although I had a momentary memory loss as regards the radio control and the VOR procedure, my mind had remained clear and sound. I knew that the airspeed must be retained and any vigorous movements of the controls to the ailerons or rudder would cause the plane to stall. Nothing else at that moment mattered.

According to the altimeter I was at an altitude of two

thousand feet but again I wasn't able to perform the simple task such as resetting the altimeter to the universal setting of 29.92 which would then show me, with reasonable accuracy, what my true altitude was. My body's coordination failed me again.

I wouldn't say that I felt numb, but to perform any other actions had become impossible. I was in a sort of drunken stupor whereby I wanted to talk to air traffic control but my mind was telling me not to. I was convinced that I was in some sort of trance that had impaired my thought processes. Every task had become more and more difficult to perform. Again hypoxia was out of the question since the altitude of the plane hadn't been high enough.

I tried to think clearly but voices in my head were clouding my judgement. To this day I can clearly remember those voices. They seemed to be not of this world. Never before in my entire life had I heard such words. I can't even remember if the words were spoken or some sort of subconscious suggestion which I unwillingly followed. I noticed that the altimeter was showing a continued descent and I wasn't at that stage able to do anything about it. What and whoever had control over me wanted me to do everything opposite to what I tried to do. The only comparison I can make is the experience I had had when waking up after an operation under general anaesthetic.

I still had no fear and was convinced that the voices would somehow disappear in the next few moments as quickly as they had appeared. The suggestions did stop but my ability to think about operating the flight controls and to establish radio contact, which was vital, remained the same. I just couldn't remember how to tune in to any frequency. The altimeter was showing an altitude of fifteen hundred feet and descending, but I knew that the plane was actually much lower.

I had to gain some height immediately. As I tried to apply more power, the engine began to misfire and splutter. I reduced the power and the engine stopped misfiring and again I slowly regained some control of my mind. I applied the carburettor heater and tried to alternate the revs. The engine stabilised and I visually checked my actual height. The shocking truth hit me. I was flying just above the ground! Maybe some thirty feet.

My ability to think clearly came back again in a flash. I pushed the lever to full power and raised the plane's nose upwards. The next thing I remember is seeing three ropes that looked like lines appearing in front of the plane's nose and coming closer and closer. They were:

HIGH VOLTAGE WIRE POWER LINES!

It dawned on me that while I had been trying to tune up the engine, I had forgotten that I had entered these power lines into my flight plan in order to use them as a marker.

What should I do?

What was to be done?

I pushed the control column forward in order to

immediately lower the nose and at the same time watched the lines passing above the cock-pit. At any moment I expected the lowest wire to slice through the aft of the plane. I must have closed my eyes for a few moments and waited for an explosion.

I opened my eyes and looked ahead. I was about thirty or forty feet above the ground. I turned my head around to see the cables behind me. I had obviously missed the lower power line by a few inches. The clarity of my thinking had miraculously returned. The ground below me had become familiar and I had worked out that Lake Okeechobee was only two miles away. I increased the power and raised the nose again in order to gain a higher altitude. I tuned into the ATC frequency and requested permission to land at Okee Chobee Regional Airport. I was asked whether it was an emergency landing. "Negative" I replied.

After a lengthy conversation with the ATC and control tower, I managed to land safely. I was advised to come to the airport's operational offices. As I shut the engine down and did all the after-landing checks, I noticed that the strobe warning light at the top of the tail section was barely attached to the casing. I must have touched one of the power lines after all! Why had I not been electrocuted? How was I going to explain everything? What would happen to my newly gained pilot's licence?

I walked towards the terminal with mixed emotions. One thing was certain. I would, under no circumstances, tell the controllers what had really happened, knowing how ridiculed other pilots had been in the past when they had claimed to be influenced by some kind of paranormal force. Besides, I had no real evidence of any actual unidentified powers that had led me to a near collision with the power lines.

However, I would have to mention the cause of the partially sheared off warning light to the chief flight instructor. The questioning followed for the next two days. The power line had to be checked out as well. I had prepared myself for the revocation of my licence. On the second inspection the investigators found an electrical fault which had blacked out the critical instruments during my flight. But to this day I still believe that the electrical fault, the loss of time and the host of other things which occurred were caused by something unknown. Luckily, my licence was not revoked but I was warned of shortcomings on my part.

To this day I have no explanation for the forces that influenced my mind during that fateful flight. It was like an invisible UFO had put its tractor beam on me. I did not have an active interest in such things at the time but I kept an open mind about what actually happened. Throughout my harrowing experience on that cloudless day, I did not actually see anything supernatural, but I definitely felt forces that rendered me powerless for nearly thirty minutes.

1

The Last Life

I am happy to say, there *is* no ninth chapter....